VOL **21** URA-ZOO
1759–1846

FUNK & WAGNALLS **new**

ENCYCLOPEDIA OF SCIENCE

FUNK & WAGNALLS, INC.

HOW TO USE FUNK & WAGNALLS NEW ENCYCLOPEDIA OF SCIENCE

Volumes 1 through 21 have information printed on the front covers, spine, and title pages that make it easy to find the articles you want to read.

- Volume numbers are printed in all three places in Volumes 1 through 21.
- Letter breaks — $\frac{COL}{DIA}$ — are printed in all three places in Volumes 1 through 21. The letters above the line are the first three letters of the first article title in the volume. The letters below the line are the first three letters of the last article title in the volume.
- Page breaks — $\frac{351}{438}$ — are printed on the spines and title pages of Volumes 1 through 21. They provide the page numbers of the first and last text pages in the volume.

Articles are arranged alphabetically by title in Volumes 1 through 21. Most titles are printed in **BOLD-FACE CAPITAL** letters. Some titles are printed in even larger letters.

- Some titles are not article titles, but refer you to the actual article title. Within articles you will find *See* or *See also* other article names for further information. All of these references to other articles are called cross-references.
- Most article titles are followed by a phonetic pronunciation. Use the Pronunciation Guide on page vi of Volume 1 to learn the correct pronunciation of the article title.
- At the end of most articles are two sets of initials. The first set identifies the person who wrote the article. The second set identifies the special consultant who checked the article for accuracy. All of these people are listed by their initials and full names and position on pages v and vi of Volume 1.
- This symbol at the end of an article indicates that there is a project based on the subject of the article in the Projects, Bibliography & Index volume. The project is found under its article title, and all of the project article titles are arranged alphabetically on pages 1 through 64 of the Projects, Bibliography & Index volume.

The Projects, Bibliography & Index Volume contains three sections. Each is an essential part of the encyclopedia.

- Projects based on articles in the encyclopedia are found in the first section. Each is both entertaining and educational. Each is designed for use by a student and for parental participation if desired.
- Bibliography reading lists in the second section list books under general scientific categories that are also titles of major articles. Each book listed is marked with either a YA (Young Adult) or J (Juvenile) reading level indicator. YA generally applies to readers at the junior high level or higher. J applies to readers at grade levels below junior high school.
- Index entries for all article titles plus many subjects that are not article titles are found in the third section. Instructions on using the Index are found at the start of the Index section in the Projects, Bibliography & Index volume.

URANINITE (yù rā′ nə nīt′) Uraninite is the chief source of uranium. (*See* URANIUM.) It is a mineral, made up mainly of uranium dioxide (UO_2). Uraninite usually forms black, fairly hard, dense crystals and less dense masses. The massive type is called pitchblende. (*See* PITCHBLENDE.)

Through oxidation the make up of uraninite varies between UO_2 and $UO_{2.6}$. Thorium atoms can take the place of uranium atoms in molecular structure. A complete solid-solution series extends to thorianite (ThO_2). Some varieties in this series contain amounts of rare earth elements, especially cerium. (*See* CERIUM; RARE EARTH ELEMENT.) Lead occurs in uraninite as a product from the decay of uranium and thorium by radioactivity. (*See* RADIOACTIVITY.) The amount present can be used to measure the geologic age of the mineral.

Uraninite has been obtained largely from hydrothermal vein deposits, as in the Katanga district of Zaire. Large deposits of uraninite are also found in Saxony (Germany), the Great Bear Lake (Canada), Blind River (Ontario), and the plateaus of Colorado, Utah, and New Mexico.   J.J.A./R.H.

URANIUM (yù rā′ nē əm) Uranium (U) is a silvery, radioactive, metallic element. Its atomic number is 92 and its atomic weight is 238.03. It melts at 1,132°C [2,070°F] and boils at 3,818°C [6,904°F]. The relative density of uranium is 19.0

The German chemist Martin Klaproth discovered uranium in 1789 and named it for the planet Uranus. The radioactive properties of uranium were first demonstrated by the French physicist Antoine Henry Becquerel in 1896. Becquerel used a fluorescent salt of uranium (*see* FLUORESCENCE) to produce an image on a photographic plate that he had covered with a light-absorbing substance. The investigations of radioactivity that followed Becquerel's experiments led to the discovery of radium. (*See* RADIUM.) Natural uranium is a mixture of two main isotopes, uranium-238 and uranium-235. (*See* ISOTOPE.) 99.27 percent of the uranium found in nature is uranium-238 and 0.72 percent is uranium-235. Uranium occurs as uranium oxides in the mineral pitchblende. It is also found in many other minerals. The ore is first concentrated and then treated with sulfuric acid or some other chemical. The uranium in the solution can then be separated from other substances and extracted.

The most important use for uranium is as a fuel for nuclear reactors. Either uranium metal or its compounds may be used for this. For a long time, uranium compounds were used to color glass and ceramics. Today, this process is recognized as dangerous because uranium compounds are both highly toxic and radioactive.

Nuclear reactors use a form of uranium that contains more uranium-235 than is found in natural uranium. Therefore, some of the uranium-238 has to be removed. Two common methods of doing this involve diffusion and the use of centrifugal force. (*See* CENTRIFUGE; DIFFUSION.) These processes work because the two isotopes have slightly different atomic weights.

All isotopes of uranium are radioactive. They decay to form other elements. The longest-lived isotope is uranium-238. It has a half life of 4,510 million years. The half life of uranium-235 is 710 million years. (*See* HALF LIFE.)   M.E./J.R.W.

URANUS (yùr′ ə nəs) Uranus is the third largest planet in the solar system. It is located seventh in order from the sun. Uranus has a diameter of about 52,200 km [32,500 mi]. The planet lies an average of 2,872,700,000 km [1,785,000,000 mi] from the sun. It takes Uranus about 84 years to make a complete trip around the sun. Uranus makes one complete spin on its axis every 16 hours and 48 minutes. The axis is at a 98° tilt.

The British astronomer Sir William Herschel discovered Uranus in 1781, using a telescope that he had made himself. Until the American spacecraft *Voyager 2* flew by the planet, from November 1985 through February 1986, astronomers knew little more than Herschel did about Uranus's physical characteristics. Data transmitted back to earth by *Voyager 2* revealed that Uranus has a magnetic field and that the atmosphere of the planet consists mostly of hydrogen, 10 to 15 percent helium, and lesser amounts of methane. Photographs taken by *Voyager 2* of Uranus's moons, particularly Miranda, revealed strange topographic patterns that scientists had never seen on any other body in the solar system.

Uranus has 15 moons. They orbit its equator and move with it in a clockwise direction. Also orbiting the planet's equator are 10 rings. These rings were discovered in 1977 by the American astronomer James Elliot. *See also* PLANET; SOLAR SYSTEM. J.M.C./C.R.

UREA (yu̇ rē′ ə) Urea is a nitrogen-containing organic compound. Its chemical formula is H_2NCONH_2. Urea is an end-product, or waste, of protein metabolism in mammals and some fish. (*See* METABOLISM.) It is formed in the liver and is excreted by the kidneys as part of urine. In most other animals, the end-product of protein metabolism is uric acid.

Urea was first synthesized—made artificially—in 1828 by the German chemist Friedrich Wöhler. It was the first naturally-occurring organic compound to be synthesized in the laboratory. As such, its discovery is considered to be the birth of synthetic organic chemistry.

Commercially, urea is prepared from ammonia and carbon dioxide. Because it contains so much nitrogen, urea is used in many fertilizers. (*See* FERTILIZER.) It is also added to animal feed and is used in making plastics, explosives, enamels, permanent-press fabrics, and waterproof paper. Urea is used in the drug industry to make barbiturates. Urea is sometimes called carbamide. *See also* EXCRETION; PLASTIC; URINE. A.J.C./J.M.

URETER (yu̇r′ ət ər) In mammals, birds, and reptiles, the ureter is a tube that carries urine from each kidney to a storage area called the urinary bladder. *See also* EXCRETION; KIDNEY. W.R.P./J.J.F.

URETHRA (yu̇ rē′ thrə) In most mammals, the urethra is a tube in the body that carries urine from the urinary bladder to the outside of the body. In females, it is totally separate from the reproductive system. In males, however, the vas deferens connects with the urethra. (*See* REPRODUCTIVE SYSTEM.) *See also* EXCRETION; URINE. A.J.C./J.J.F.

UREY, HAROLD CLAYTON (1893-1981) Harold Urey (yu̇r′ ē) was an American chemist. He was born at Walkerton, Indiana, and studied at the University of Montana. He began working on explosives during World War I. In 1931, Urey was at Columbia University. He began work to try to obtain heavy hydrogen. Other scientists had believed that an isotope of hydrogen ought to exist, but in very small amounts. Urey decided to try to purify heavy hydrogen by evaporating all the lighter hydrogen. He succeeded in evaporating enough ordinary hydrogen to be able to measure the heavy hydrogen that was left. Urey received the Nobel prize for chemistry in 1934 for his discovery of deuterium and his isolation of heavy water.

Urey continued to work on isotopes. He discovered how to separate uranium isotopes during World War II. Later, he became worried about the use of his own and other discoveries. He gave up work on possible weapons of war and devoted his research to geology. He helped to date fossils and developed theories of the formation of the planets. He even proposed what the atmosphere of the earth might have been like when life began. *See also* DEUTERIUM; ISOTOPE; URANIUM.

C.M./D.G.F.

URINE (yὑr′ ən) Urine is a liquid waste product of the body that the kidneys manufacture. The urine of a healthy person is amber-colored and slightly acid. It is heavier than water and has a relative density of 1.022. Urine is made up of water, urea, creatinine, uric acid, and inorganic salts. These salts include ammonia, potassium, sodium, calcium, and magnesium.

The kidneys remove waste matter and water from the blood. The substances pass to the bladder and are expelled from the body as urine. Urine is produced in larger quantities when a person drinks large amounts of liquid. When a person perspires, he or she produces less urine.

The condition of urine often explains something about a person's health. Sugar in the urine is a symptom of diabetes. Albumin and blood in the urine can mean that the kidneys have been damaged. *See also* DIABETES; KIDNEY.

W.R.P./J.J.F.

URSA MAJOR AND MINOR Ursa Major (ər′ sə mā′ jər) and Minor (mī′ nər) are two constellations that are always visible from the mid-Northern Hemisphere. They are perhaps the easiest constellations to locate.

Ursa Major, or Great Bear, contains the group of stars known as the Big Dipper. Two stars of the Big Dipper, Dubhe and Merak, point to the North Star. Ursa Major also contains the star Alcor. Alcor was used for centuries to test vision.

Ursa Minor, or Little Bear, contains the group of stars known as the Little Dipper. At the end of the handle of the "dipper" is the North Star. The North Star has been an important aid to navigators for many years. The Little Dipper is faint compared to the Big Dipper. *See also* CONSTELLATION; NORTH STAR.

J.M.C./C.R.

UTERUS (yüt′ ə rəs) The uterus, or womb, is a hollow organ that is part of the female reproductive system. It is shaped like an upside-down pear. Its lowest section, the cervix, is a necklike opening to the vagina, or birth canal. (*See* VAGINA.) In its upper section are the openings to the two fallopian tubes.

The uterus is made of three layers of muscles that are intertwined with many fibers and blood vessels. The inside of the uterus is lined with a moist, mucous membrane called the endometrium. The thickness of the endometrium changes during the menstrual cycle. (*See* MENSTRUAL CYCLE.) It is thickest at the time of ovulation when the egg is released from an ovary. In preparation for a fertilized egg, the endometrium swells with added blood, proteins, glucose, and minerals. If the egg is fertilized, it implants in the endometrium and begins developing. (*See* IMPLANTATION.) Development continues in the uterus until the baby is born, some nine months later. (*See* PREGNANCY.) If the egg is not fertilized, it and the outer lining of the endometrium are released through the vagina during menstrual bleeding. *See also* FERTILIZATION; REPRODUCTION; REPRODUCTIVE SYSTEM.

A.J.C./J.J.F.

VACCINATION (vak′ sə nā′ shən) Vaccination is the placement of dead or weakened germs into the body. This causes the body to develop resistance to a disease. The material, which is usually injected, is called a vaccine. The term vaccination comes from the Latin word "vacca," meaning cow. Edward Jenner, the first person to use vaccination, used cowpox germs to give resistance to smallpox.

Vaccine causes the body to produce substances called antibodies. Antibodies fight the effect of bacteria, toxins, and viruses. (*See*

ANTIBODY.) Vaccines must be strong enough to cause the body to develop resistance to a disease. They must also be weak enough so that they do not infect the body or cause serious illness.

Effective vaccines have been developed against many diseases, such as cholera, measles, mumps, polio, rabies, typhoid fever, and smallpox. (*See* CHOLERA; MEASLES; TYPHOID FEVER; SMALLPOX.) *See also* IMMUNITY; JENNER, EDWARD; SALK, JONAS.   J.J.A./J.J.F.

This statue commemorates Jenner in one of his early vaccination experiments. The small boy shown here is said to be his son, but there is no evidence that this is so.

VACUOLE (vak′ yə wōl′) A vacuole usually is fluid-filled space in a cell. It is enclosed by a membrane that separates it from the surrounding cytoplasm. (*See* MEMBRANE.) Many, though not all, cells have vacuoles. In protozoa, food vacuoles "eat," digest, and excrete food. Contractile vacuoles squirt out excess water. Some vacuoles, particularly in microorganisms, contain gases instead of fluids. *See also* CELL; MICROORGANISM.

A.J.C./E.R.L.

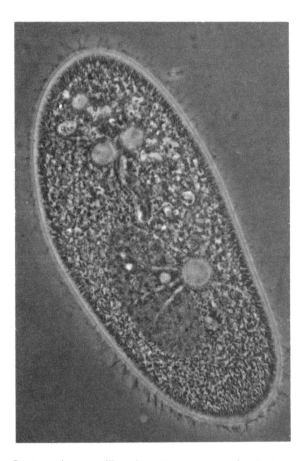

Paramecium, a ciliated protozoan, contains two kinds of vacuoles. Contractile vacuoles, of which one can be seen here, are star-shaped. The other vacuoles are food vacuoles.

VACUUM (vak′ yüm) A vacuum is a space that contains no matter. The easiest way to produce a vacuum is to remove the air from inside a strong container. The container has to be strong or it will collapse when the air is removed. The air can be removed by using a vacuum pump.

A vacuum has several important and useful properties. One of these is that it will not conduct heat. This property is used in the Dewar flask. A Dewar flask is used for keeping substances at a constant temperature. It is made up of a glass vessel with double walls. Between the walls there is a vacuum. This vacuum prevents any heat loss by conduction. However, the Dewar flask does lose a small amount of heat by radiation. This is because heat radiation can travel through a vacuum.

Sound is transmitted, or sent, by matter. It cannot travel through a vacuum. For example, on the moon there is very little atmosphere and astronauts must use radios to talk to one another.

A vacuum is measured by the pressure of the residual gases in it. The lower the pressure, the more perfect the vacuum. The unit of measurement is called the torr. One torr is the pressure produced by a volume of mercury one millimeter [0.04 in] high. The SI unit of pressure is the pascal. This unit is often used in vacuum measurements. (*See* INTERNATIONAL SYSTEM.)   M.E./J.D.

VACUUM TUBE (vak′ yüm tüb) A vacuum tube is an electronic device. Before the invention of transistors, vacuum tubes were used in many types of electrical equipment. A vacuum tube is made up of a glass tube. The air is pumped from the tube and it is then sealed to leave a vacuum inside. A vacuum tube also contains two electrodes. They are connected to the outside by wires that pass through the glass. Vacuum tubes may also contain metal screens called grids which are connected by wires to the outside. A vacuum tube that contains no grids is called a diode. One that has just one grid is a triode. A tetrode has two grids, and a pentode has three grids.

The simplest vacuum tube is the diode. It acts like a one-way valve, allowing current to pass only in one direction. One electrode, called the cathode, gives out small particles of electricity. These particles are called electrons. To give out electrons, the cathode has to be heated. This is done by passing a current through the cathode or through a wire filament surrounding it. The other electrode is called the anode. The anode is connected to a positive voltage, relative to the cathode. The electrons the cathode gives out will be attracted to the anode. The electrons can flow only from the cathode to the anode. They cannot flow in the opposite direction. This flow of electrons is a current passing through the tube. The current through a diode can, therefore, flow only in one direction. For this reason, diodes are used for changing an alternating current into a direct current. An alternating current flows in both directions alternately. A direct current flows in only one direction. (*See* CURRENT, ELECTRIC.) This process is called rectification. The tube is called a rectifier. (*See* RECTIFIER.)

Triodes and the other types of vacuum tubes contain grids. These grids are placed between the anode and the cathode. If a small voltage is applied to the grid, large changes can be produced in the current flowing through the tube. Such tubes are said to amplify the current. They are used as amplifiers in electrical circuits. (*See* AMPLIFIER.)

Transistors have for the most part taken the place of vacuum tubes. (*See* TRANSISTOR.) Transistors are better because they are sturdier, take up less space, and use less current. However, vacuum tubes are still used in high-power amplifiers and rectifiers.

M.E./A.I.

VALENCE (vā′ ləns) Atoms combine together in groups called molecules. In a molecule, the atoms are held together by chemical bonds. The valence of an element is the number of chemical bonds that its atoms can form. (*See* BOND, CHEMICAL.) For example, hydrogen has a valence of one. Therefore, its atoms each have one bond for combining with other atoms. Carbon has a valence of four and can form four bonds. Therefore, four atoms of hydrogen can combine with one atom of carbon to form a compound called methane. Its chemical formula, CH_4, shows that each molecule of methane contains one atom of carbon and four atoms of hydrogen.

Many elements have more than one valence. Iron, for example, can have a valence of either two or three. This means that it can form either of two compounds when it combines with another element. Chlorine has a valence of one. Iron and chlorine can form

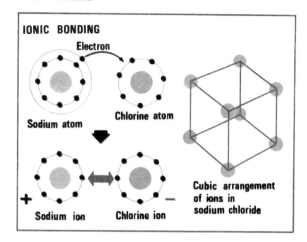

IONIC BONDING

Electron

Sodium atom

Chlorine atom

+

Sodium ion

Chlorine ion

Cubic arrangement of ions in sodium chloride

Ionic bonding is shown by sodium chloride, in which the sodium atom (Na) gives an electron to the chlorine atom (Cl).

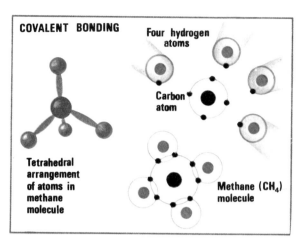

COVALENT BONDING

Four hydrogen atoms

Carbon atom

Tetrahedral arrangement of atoms in methane molecule

Methane (CH_4) molecule

Covalent bonding is shown by a methane molecule, in which each of the four hydrogen atoms shares its single electron with one of the four outer electrons of the carbon atom.

two different compounds. One is called iron (II) chloride, or ferrous chloride. Its formula is $FeCl_2$. In this compound, iron has a valence of two. The other compound is called iron (III) chloride, or ferric chloride. Its formula is $FeCl_3$. Here, iron has a valence of three.

A group of atoms may also have a valence. Such a group is called a radical. (*See* RADICAL.) An example is the sulfate radical. It has the formula SO_4 and has a valence of two. With iron, it forms either iron (II) sulfate ($FeSO_4$) or iron (III) sulfate ($Fe_2(SO_4)_3$). An atom or radical with a valence of one is said to be univalent. It it has a valence of two, it is called divalent. A trivalent atom or radical has a valence of three.

Sometimes, the valence of an element can be figured from the formulas of its compounds. For example, calcium forms the compound calcium sulfate, $CaSO_4$. The valence of the sulfate radical is two. Therefore, it follows that the valence of calcium is also two because one atom of calcium combines with one sulfate radical. However, this does not always work. Carbon and hydrogen form a compound called ethane. Its formula is C_2H_6. Since hydrogen has a valence of one, it seems as though carbon has a valence of three in ethane. However, the actual arrangement of

the atoms in a molecule of ethane is like this:

$$
\begin{array}{ccc}
\text{H} & & \text{H} \\
| & & | \\
\text{H}-\text{C}&-&\text{C}-\text{H} \\
| & & | \\
\text{H} & & \text{H}
\end{array}
$$

The carbon atom still has four bonds and, therefore, has a valence of four.   M.E./J.D.

VAMPIRE BAT (vam′ pīr bat) The vampire bat is a small bat that attacks cattle, fowl, and other warm-blooded animals, and drinks their blood. Vampire bats belong to the bat family (Desmodontidae). They live in tropical Central and South America.

The common vampire bat is a reddish brown animal about 8 cm [3 in] long. It has very sharp teeth in the shape of triangles that cut like a razor. Vampire bats sometimes attack persons who are sleeping. The bite itself of a vampire bat is not serious, and the bat takes only a small amount of blood. The bite heals quickly. However, many vampire bats carry rabies, a disease which is fatal if not treated in time. Cattle and other large animals are more often attacked by vampire bats than humans are. Cattle living in areas where there are vampire bats are often inoculated against rabies. *See also* BAT.   W.R.P./J.J.M.

A vampire bat has sharp teeth, with which it slashes its victim's skin.

VANADIUM (və nād′ ē əm) Vanadium (V) is a hard, silvery, metallic element. Its atomic number is 23 and its atomic weight is 50.94. It melts at 1,890°C [3,430°F] and boils at 3,380°C [6, 120°F]. Its relative density is 6.1. The Swedish chemist Nils Sefstrom discovered vanadium in 1830. It is a fairly rare element and is found in the minerals vanadinite and carnotite. Vanadium is one of the hardest of all metals and is added to steel to increase its strength. Vanadium forms an oxide called Vanadium pentoxide (V_2O_5). Vanadium pentoxide is important as a catalyst in industry. (*See* CATALYST.)   M.E./J.R.W.

VAN ALLEN, JAMES ALFRED (1914–   ) James Van Allen (van al′ ən) is as American physicist. He was born at Mount Pleasant, Iowa. He has been head of the physics department at the University of Iowa since 1951. During World War II, Van Allen was one of the many scientists working on military problems. He developed a fuse that uses radio waves to detect when it is near a target. After the war, Van Allen used military rockets for investigating cosmic rays.

Van Allen continued his work on cosmic rays. He analyzed the results of tests made by equipment on space rockets in the 1950s. The early cosmic ray detectors on space ships seemed to show that the rays stopped suddenly. But Van Allen designed a detector shielded with lead to protect it. This showed that there is an enormous amount of deadly radiation in space. In the earth's atmosphere, radiation seems to be trapped near the equator. There are regions, which have been called the Van Allen belts, where most of the radiation is found. It is the earth's magnetic field that traps particles which absorb radiation from space. Some experiments were done to prove this, but scientists like Van Allen now realize that it is dangerous to risk upsetting our protective atmosphere. *See also* RADIATION.   C.M./D.G.F.

VAN ALLEN BELTS (van al′ ən belt) The Van Allen belts are zones of intense radiation that surround the earth like irregularly-shaped doughnuts. They are named for James Van Allen, an American scientist, who discovered them in 1958. The inner belt is dense and is about 3,200 km [2,000 mi] above the earth. The outer belt is also dense and about 16,000 to 19,300 km [10,000 to 12,000 mi] above the earth.

The inner belt, which contains the most energy, consists of protons and electrons. The outer belt contains mostly electrons. These charged particles probably originate from a thin stream of gases thrown off by the sun. The particles produce X rays that can be harmful to humans. Spacecraft flying through the Van Allen belts must be shielded to protect the astronauts against these X rays. *See also* X RAY. W.R.P./C.R.

VAN DE GRAAFF GENERATOR (van′ də graf′ jen′ ə rāt′ ər)

A Van de Graaff generator is a machine that is used for producing very high voltages. It contains a moving belt that runs around two pulleys, one above the other. Near the bottom pulley there are a number of fine needles with their points close to the belt. These needles are connected to a potential of 10,000 to 50,000 volts. The moving belt picks up a charge from the needles and carries it to the top of the generator. The upper pulley is at the center of a large metal dome. More needles around the top of the pulley collect the charge from the belt. These needles are connected to the dome. The charges flow from the needles to the dome. As the charge builds up, a potential difference of several million volts is produced between the dome and earth.

The dome must be well insulated and the air around it must be dry. Since water conducts electricity, moisture in the air could discharge the dome. Walls or other objects near the dome could also discharge the

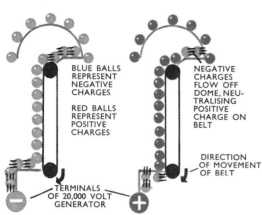

When a Van de Graaff generator is charging negatively (left), negative charges (shown by blue balls) flow from the negative terminal to the moving belt via the lower spikes. If the generator is charging positively (right), negative charges flow off the dome and are replaced by positive charges coming from the positive terminal of the 20,000 volt electric generator.

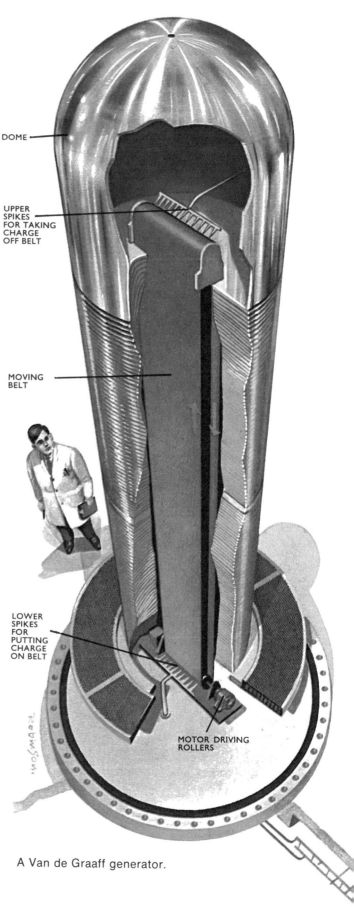

A Van de Graaff generator.

generator. When the generator discharges, the effect is like a flash of lightning.

Modern generators are enclosed in a steel tank containing gas at a pressure of about 20 to 30 atmospheres. This helps reduce the chance of an accidental discharge. Van de Graaff generators are used by physicists for accelerating particles such as electrons to very high speeds. (*See* ACCELERATOR, PARTICLE.)

M.E./J.D.

VAN DER WAALS, JOHANNES (1837–1923) Johannes van der Waals (van′ dər wȯlz′) was a Dutch physicist. He was born at Leiden and studied at the university there. He was interested in the physics of gases and liquids. He knew of the work of Boyle and Charles and set out to find out why their equations did not exactly match the way gases and liquids behave. He worked out that the size of molecules, together with forces between molecules, affect their behavior. Even though gas molecules are extremely small, each is a different size. This affects the way molecules of different gases behave. The forces between molecules in a gas are called van der Waals forces. In 1910 van der Waals was awarded the Nobel Prize for Physics for this work.

C.M./D.G.F.

VAN DER WAALS FORCES (van′ dər wȯlz′ fōrs′ əs) Van der Waals forces are forces that act between molecules. They are named after the Dutch physicist, Johannes van der Waals. In 1873, he produced an equation that related the pressure and temperature of a gas to its volume. He assumed that the pressure would be a little larger than previous equations predicted. This is because of forces of attraction between the molecules of the gas. His equation was more accurate than earlier equations and scientists realized that these forces did exist. Van der Waals forces are very weak. They act only when the molecules are close together. (*See* VAN DER WAALS, JOHANNES.)

M.E./J.D.

VAPOR (vā′ pər) Below a certain temperature, almost all gases can be changed into liquid by applying enough pressure. The only exception is the gas helium. However, above this temperature, no amount of pressure will cause a gas to liquefy. This temperature is called the critical temperature of the gas. It is different for different gases. (*See* CRITICAL TEMPERATURE.) A vapor is a gas that is below its critical temperature. In other words, it is a gas that can be liquefied by pressure alone. Like all gases, vapors exert a pressure. This pressure is known as vapor pressure. (*See* VAPOR PRESSURE.)

M.E./J.D.

VAPOR PRESSURE (vā′ pər presh′ ər) Below a certain temperature, a gas can be changed into liquid by applying enough pressure. Above this temperature, no amount of pressure will cause the gas to liquefy. This temperature is called the critical temperature of the gas. A gas below its critical temperature is called a vapor. (*See* VAPOR.) Since it is a gas, a vapor exerts a pressure. This is called the vapor pressure.

All liquids, and even solids, exert a vapor pressure. This is caused by the molecules in the liquid escaping into the atmosphere. This is why a pool of liquid evaporates. However, if the liquid is kept in a container, it will not evaporate. As the vapor pressure builds up, the vapor molecules in the air tend to return to the liquid. At a certain pressure, the same number of molecules enter the liquid as leave it. This is the vapor pressure of the liquid. It is the maximum pressure of the vapor.

The vapor pressure of a liquid increases with temperature. Eventually, at a certain temperature, the vapor pressure of the liquid is equal to the pressure of the atmosphere. At this temperature, the liquid boils. If the atmospheric pressure increases or decreases, the boiling point of the liquid increases or decreases. For example, at high altitudes, atmospheric pressure is less than it is at sea level. At the higher altitudes, the boiling point of water is less than the 100°C [212°F] it is at sea level.   M.E./J.D.

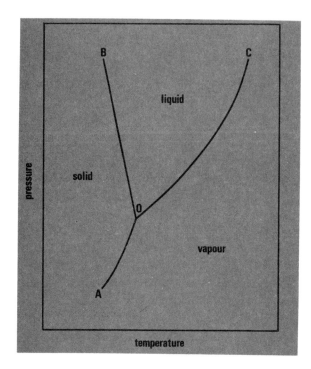

This diagram shows the relationship between the vapor pressure and the temperature of water. At low temperatures, water is generally a solid (ice). At higher temperatures and pressures, water becomes a liquid. However, if the temperature is increased or if the pressure is reduced, water will become a vapor. The line OC shows the points at which the liquid and vapor are in equilibrium. Point O is called the triple point and is the unique point at which the vapor, liquid, and solid exist together.

VARIABLE STAR (ver′ ē ə bəl stär′) A variable star is a star whose light changes from bright to dim to bright again. There are several causes for this type of change.

Some stars expand (grow larger) and contract (grow smaller) at regular intervals. These stars are called pulsating variables. The time between expansions is known as the star's period. The North Star is a pulsating variable with a period of about 4 days. Any variable star with a period of less than 50 days

is called a short period variable, or a Cepheid variable. Many Cepheid variables are yellow supergiants. Some pulsating variables have periods longer than 100 days. These are called long period variables. Irregular variables have no set period.

Some stars have great explosions that increase their brightness millions of times. These are called exploding stars, or novae. (*See* NOVA.) The increased brightness may last for a few days, weeks, or even years. Eventually, the star returns to its previous brilliance. Extremely bright exploding stars are called supernovae. (*See* SUPERNOVA.)

Double stars are two stars that revolve around each other. One of them occasionally blocks the light of the other. Such a double star is called an eclipsing binary. Eclipsing binaries are not considered true variables because internal processes of these stars are not responsible for their variation of light. *See also* STAR.   J.M.C./C.R.

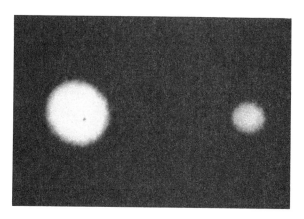

This double exposure photograph of a variable star shows how the brightness of the star changes.

VARNISH (vär′ nish) Varnish is a transparent liquid (one that can be seen through) often applied on wood, metal, and other materials for protection. Varnish protects objects chiefly from air and moisture. It is also used for decorative purposes. After being brushed or sprayed onto the surface of an object, the varnish dries, leaving behind a hard and often glossy film.

A "clear varnish" protects the surface of wood. It also allows the natural grain of the wood to show through. "Varnish stains" contain dyes. These dyes change the color of the wood, but they also bring out the grain of the wood. Varnishes used on metal are frequently called lacquers. (*See* LACQUER.) In certain cases, varnish is used to protect insulating wires and paper from moisture. Varnishes can be baked on. Baking improves the wearing ability of the object.

There are two main kinds of varnish. Spirit varnishes are made of resins. (*See* RESIN.) Shellac is a common spirit varnish. (*See* SHELLAC.) Oleoresinous varnishes are mixtures of resins and drying oils. These substances are heated and dissolved in turpentine or petroleum products. Oleoresinous varnishes can withstand outdoor conditions well. Spar varnish, used on the brightwork of boats, is an oleoresinous varnish. Varnishes used on surfaces exposed to weather contain more oil than the varnishes used indoors.   J.J.A./J.M.

VASCULAR PLANT (vas′ kyə lər plant′) Vascular plants have a special transport system in their roots, stems, and leaves. This vascular system is made of tissues called xylem and phloem. Xylem carries water and dissolved minerals from where they are absorbed (roots) to where they are used in photosynthesis (leaves). Phloem carries dis-

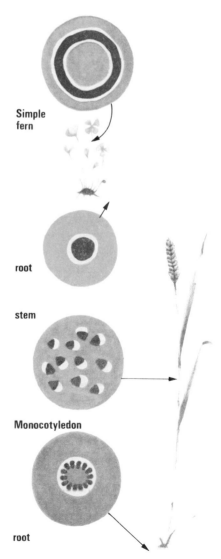

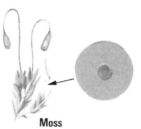

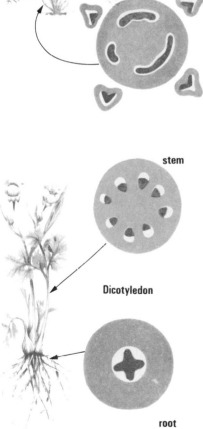

Some non-vascular plants, such as mosses (above), have a central core of differentiated cells, but the function of these cells is not known. The simplest vascular structure is found in the roots of simple ferns (above left), where a central core of xylem (red) is surrounded by a ring of phloem (yellow). In the stems of these ferns the xylem forms a ring, with phloem both inside and outside. Where leaves branch off, this ring is broken, and in the most advanced ferns (above right), the vascular tissue appears as a number of bundles whose structure is the same as the simple fern. In angiosperms the vascular tissues are broken up into bundles. In monocotyledons (left) these are distributed randomly, but in dicotyledons (right) they are arranged in a ring.

Simple fern

root

stem

Monocotyledon

root

Moss

Higher fern

stem

Dicotyledon

root

solved food and other substances from where they are produced (leaves) to all other parts of the plant. In addition to its transport function, the vascular system gives the plant strength and support.

The vascular plants include the ferns, club mosses, horsetails, gymnosperms, and angiosperms. Most of these plants live on land and all belong to the plant phylum Tracheophyta. *See also* PHLOEM; PLANT KINGDOM; XYLEM.   A.J.C./M.H.S.

VECTOR QUANTITY (vek′ tər kwänt′ ət ē) A vector quantity is any quantity that has both magnitude (or size) and direction. An example of a vector quantity is velocity. Velocity is speed in a certain direction. Two airplanes flying across the sky toward each other can have the same speed. But their velocities will be different because they are traveling in opposite directions. But three planes flying in formation will have the same speed and velocity. Another example of a vector quantity is force. For example, the force of gravity always acts downward, toward the center of the earth.

A vector quantity can be simply shown by a line. The length of the line stands for the size of the vector. The direction of the vector is shown by the direction of the line. An arrowhead is placed on the line to show which way the vector acts along the line. For example, two forces, F_1 and F_2, can be shown as follows:

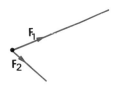

These two forces are acting at a single point, shown by a black dot. If they are both acting on one body, then the body moves as if a single force acted upon it. This single force is a combination of the two forces. It is called

the resultant of the two forces. It is found by adding the two vectors together. Since vectors have direction, they cannot be added as though they were simple numbers. To add two vectors, place them so that the head of one is touching the tail of the other. Then draw a line connecting the two free ends. This line is the resultant vector quantity.

The addition of vectors is very important in deciding the course of an aircraft. Suppose an aircraft is flying from town A to town B. There is also a wind blowing at right-angles to this direction. The aircraft has to head into the wind a little to compensate for this. Therefore, the aircraft heads toward the point C.

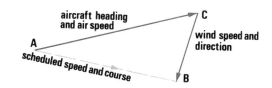

Suppose there are three forces acting on a body. If, when the vectors are added, the head of one touches the tail of another, there is no resultant force. The forces balance each other out. The body is said to be in equilibrium.

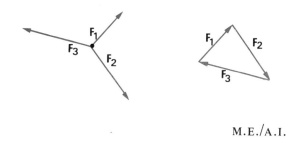

M.E./A.I.

VEGETABLE (vej′ tə bəl) A vegetable is any non-reproductive part of a plant that can be eaten. The reproductive parts of a plant— flowers, fruits, seeds—are usually not considered to be vegetables. (*See* FRUIT.) By this definition, such foods as cucumbers, tomatoes, beans, peas, and corn are really fruits, even though most people think of them as vegetables.

Some vegetables, such as lettuce and cabbage, are leaves. Others, such as rhubarb and asparagus, are stems. Some, such as carrots and beets, are roots. Still others, such as potatoes, are underground stems.

Usually vegetables are a good source of vitamins, minerals, and bulk. They also provide small amounts of proteins, fats, and carbohydrates, though not as much as provided by an equal amount of fruit or meat. Vegetables make up one of the four major food groups and are an important part of a balanced diet. *See also* DIET; FOOD.   A.J.C./F.W.S.

VEGETATIVE PROPAGATION (vej′ ə tāt′ iv präp′ ə gā′ shən) Vegetative propagation is the production of a complete new plant from part of another plant. It is the regeneration (making again) of all the structures of a plant from a piece such as a stem, leaf, or root. (*See* REGENERATION.) Vegetative propagation is a type of asexual reproduction in plants.

Many plants, such as the strawberry, have stems that grow along the surface of the ground. These stems are called runners, or stolons. The runners produce roots that grow into the ground. New leaves appear and, when the runners are cut or die away, there are several new plants around the original one. Some plants, such as grasses, have underground stems called rhizomes. These propagate in the same way as runners.

Some plants produce tiny buds that fall off and begin to grow. These buds, called bulbils, have a better chance of growing than do

In grafting, a scion twig is inserted into a cut in the bark of the rootstock, where it will grow, forming its own flowers and fruits.

In budding, a bud is inserted into the host plant, where it will grow and develop in a manner similar to grafting.

seeds. In some plants, the bulbils even start to grow before they fall from the parent.

Artificial vegetative propagation Farmers, gardeners, and florists often use vegetative propagation to produce many plants that are exactly the same as the original, parent plant. The major artificial methods are cutting, grafting, layering, and budding.

In cutting, a small part (usually a stem) is cut from a growing plant and placed in water or moist soil. In most cases, the cutting develops roots and grows into a complete plant. In another type of cutting, a bud is removed and planted. For example, a potato can be cut into several pieces, each of which has an eye (bud). If these pieces are planted, each will grow into a new potato plant. Grafting is similar to cutting, except the plant part is attached, or grafted, onto another plant. The cutting, or plant part, is called a scion, and the rooted plant to which it is attached is called a stock. The vascular tissues must be lined up so that they will grow together. (*See* VASCULAR PLANT.) The stock becomes the new plant's roots and the scion becomes the upper part, with its growing branches, flowers, and fruits. Many kinds of apples are grown this way.

There are two types of layering: mound and aerial. In mound layering, soil is piled up around the stem or branches of a plant. Roots grow from the stem or branch into the soil. These rooted parts can then be cut off and planted. In aerial layering, a slice is made into a stem or branch, near a bud. The whole area is then packed with sphagnum moss and covered with a waterproof wrapping. Roots grow into the moss. This part can then be cut off and planted.

Budding is much like grafting. A bud is cut from one plant and inserted into the stem of another plant. As long as their cambiums are in contact, the bud will grow. (*See* CAMBIUM.) In this way, it is possible to have one plant with several kinds of flowers or fruits.

Advantages of vegetative propagation The plants produced by vegetative propagation are the same as the parent plant. (*See* CLONE.) In many cases, they are stronger than the original. If a desirable plant has poor roots, it is possible to save it by vegetative propagation. Some plants have been bred to produce seedless fruits. Vegetative propagation is the only way to continue these varieties. Some plants are resistant to certain diseases or other dangerous substances. These can be continued by vegetative propagation. *See also* AGRONOMY; ASEXUAL REPRODUCTION.   A.J.C./M.H.S

VEIN (vān) A vein is a blood vessel, or tube, that carries blood toward the heart. Blood circulates through the body through a system of tubes. There are three kinds of tubes: arteries, capillaries, and veins. Arteries and

The leaves of dicotyledonous plants have a network of veins.

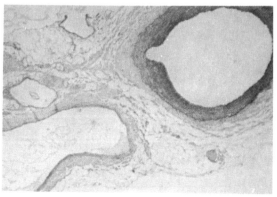

Cross sections of a mammalian vein (bottom left) and an artery (top right).

capillaries carry blood from the heart to the various parts of the body. Veins return the blood after it has nourished the tissues and taken on waste products. Most of the returning blood contains little oxygen and is therefore purplish red in color. Blood from the pulmonary veins, which lead from the lungs to the heart, contains more oxygen and is consequently bright red. Venous blood, as it is called, is under low pressure and flows slowly. It oozes rather than spurts from a cut. (*See* CIRCULATORY SYSTEM.)

The walls of veins have three layers: elastic, muscular, and lining. Veins are thinner and less muscular than arteries. Capillaries are the smallest of the three kinds of tubes. Veins in arms and legs have valves that prevent the back-flow and pooling of blood due to gravity.

Veins that are swollen, stretched, or coiled on themselves are called varicose veins. These can sometimes be found on the legs of people who do a lot of walking in their jobs and on the legs of older people. Phlebitis is a disease of the veins. In this disease, a blood clot may form in a vein and cause severe pain and stiffness. *See also* ARTERY; HEART. W.R.P./J.J.F.

VELOCITY (və läs′ ət ē) The speed of a body is the rate at which it changes its position. (*See* SPEED.) Velocity is speed in a certain direction. If two bodies are moving at the same rate but in different direction, their speeds are the same but their velocities are different. Because velocity depends on direction, it is called a vector quantity. (*See* VECTOR QUANTITY.)

There are two kinds of velocity: linear velocity and angular velocity. Linear velocity is velocity in a straight line. It is measured in units such as meters per second or kilometers per hour. Angular velocity is the velocity of a body that is moving in a circle. It is measured in degrees per second, revolutions per minute, or other units. M.E./A.I.

VENA CAVA (vē′ nə kā′ və) The vena cava is either of the two veins that carry blood back to the heart. The venae cavae (plural of vena cava) are the largest veins in the body.

The superior vena cava drains blood from the head and arms. The inferior vena cava drains blood from the legs and trunk. The superior vena cava empties its blood into the upper right chamber of the heart, known as the right atrium. The inferior vena cava also empties blood into the right atrium, at a point below the opening for the superior vena cava. *See also* BLOOD; HEART. J.M.C./J.J.F.

VENEREAL DISEASE (və nir′ ē əl diz ēz′) A venereal disease is any of several diseases that are usually spread by sexual intercourse or other kinds of sexual contact. These diseases are caused by many different kinds of organisms, including bacteria, viruses, a variety of yeast, and a type of protozoan. Several of these diseases are epidemic, including gonorrhea (bacterial), genital herpes (viral), chlamydia (bacterial), trichomonas (protozoan), and moniliasis (yeast). Syphilis, formerly epidemic, was brought under control by the widespread use of antibiotics. Currently, doctors are trying to find a cure for a newly recognized sexually transmitted disease called AIDS (acquired immune deficiency syndrome), first reported in the early 1980s. Research indicated that AIDS may be caused by two retroviruses, the first ever found in humans. (*See* VIRUS.) In many cases, though, the infected person may not even know that he or she has the disease. Even when there are no noticeable symptoms, however, all venereal diseases damage internal tissues and organs.

Since the mid-1950s, there has been a general increase in reported cases of venereal diseases. Most health authorities agree that these are only a small percentage of the actual number of cases. Public health clinics try to stop the spread of venereal disease by locating people who have had sexual contact with an infected person and seeing if these people also need treatment. If untreated, a venereal disease can cause serious sickness, permanent damage, or death. In addition, an infected person continues spreading the disease for as long as it remains untreated. *See also* GONORRHEA; SYPHILIS. A.J.C./J.J.F.

VENUS (vē′ nəs) Venus, the second planet from the sun, is also the closest planet to the earth. Venus and earth resemble each other in size only. Venus has many other characteristics that make it unique among the planets.

Characteristics of Venus Venus has a diameter of 12,112 km [7,526 mi], which is slightly smaller than that of the earth. Venus averages 108,230,000 km [67,250,000 mi] away from the sun. It makes one complete trip around the sun every 225 days. While all the other planets follow elliptical orbits around the sun, Venus follows a nearly circular path. During its trip around the sun, Venus comes within 38.9 million km [24.2 million mi] of the earth.

Venus passes through phases similar to those of the moon. These phases, which can be seen through a telescope, were first observed by the Italian astronomer Galileo. At its closest approach to the earth, Venus is barely visible because its sunlit side faces away from the earth. As it moves away from the earth, sunlit areas of Venus come into view. When it is close to the opposite side of the sun, almost all of the sunlit side is visible. Venus is called the morning star when it appears in the east at sunrise, and the evening star when it is in the west at sunset.

Venus makes one spin on its axis every 243 days. This means that a "day" on Venus is longer than the Venus "year." The planet's axis is at a 10° tilt. Venus is the only planet with a retrograde rotation. This means that Venus rotates in a direction opposite to its

orbit around the sun.

The surface of Venus is completely obscured by a thick, cloud-filled atmosphere of carbon dioxide and nitrogen. Using radar, astronomers have mapped the surface and discovered a variety of landforms, including giant impact craters like those on the moon, as well as volcanoes, plains, ridges, and canyons. Surface temperatures average about 459°C [858°F], the highest in the solar system. Solar energy, in the form of heat, is trapped by the carbon dioxide in the atmosphere. This has produced an extreme "greenhouse effect." (*See* CLIMATE.) If there ever was water on the surface of Venus, it has long since evaporated into space. Instead of water vapor, the clouds of Venus consist of droplets of sulfuric acid.

Venus has a mass equal to about 80 percent of the earth's mass. Venus has slightly less density and gravity than the earth. Venus has no moons.

Space probes to Venus Venus was the first planet to be studied by a space probe. In 1962, the American probe Mariner II made various scientific measurements of Venus. In 1966, Venera 2 and Venera 3, two Russian space probes, studied Venus. In October 1967, the American Mariner V and the Russian Venera 4 both found huge amounts of carbon dioxide in the atmosphere. Mariner X in 1974 found that Venus has an extremely weak magnetic field. In 1975, Venera 9, an unmanned Russian space probe, landed on the surface of Venus. Venera 9 took the first close range photographs of the planet's surface. Also in 1975, Venera 10 measured the planet's barometric (air) pressure. Venera 10 found the pressure to be about 95 kg per cm^2 [1,352 lb per in^2]. This is nearly 100 times greater than the earth's barometric pressure. *See also* PLANET; SOLAR SYSTEM. J.M.C./C.R.

VENUS'S-FLYTRAP (vē′ nəs flī′ trap′) Venus's-flytrap (*Dionaea muscipula*) is a perennial, carnivorous plant (one feeding on meat) native to marshy areas of North and South Carolina. It produces a 20 to 30 cm [8 to 12 in] stem that ends in an umbel (cluster) of small white flowers. Its leaves are almost circular and about 10 cm [4 in] long. They are hinged along the midline and edged with spinelike hairs. The two halves, or lobes, of these modified leaves can fold together to trap an insect. Each lobe has special glands that secrete a red digestive fluid. Each lobe also has three sensitive hairs. If one or more of these hairs is touched by an insect, the lobes snap shut in less than half a second. (*See* MOVEMENT OF PLANTS.) Once a victim has been trapped, it is digested inside the closed leaf, releasing nitrogen and other vital nutrients. The entire digestion process takes about 10 days, after which the trap reopens. *See also* CARNIVOROUS PLANT. A.J.C./M.H.S.

Venus's-flytrap is a specialized plant that captures insects in its traplike leaves. It needs insects for the nitrogen contained in their bodies.

VERNIER SCALE (vər′ nē ər skāl′) A vernier scale is a scale used in certain measuring instruments. These instruments have a scale marked on them and a pointer to show the length of the thing being measured. Very often, the pointer comes to rest between two of the divisions of the scale. For example, the pointer may read between 7 and 8 on the scale. Therefore, the correct reading may be any number between 7.1 and 7.9. It is possible to judge by eye what the final reading should be, but this is not very accurate. A vernier scale shows exactly what the correct reading should be.

The vernier scale is a small sliding scale that moves alongside the main scale. It contains divisions from 0 to 10. The zero division gives a rough indication of the measurement. If the zero division lies between 7 and 8 on the main scale, then the measurement is between 7 and 8. The divisions on the vernier scale are a little smaller than the divisions on the main scale. Therefore, only one of the divisions on the vernier scale lines up with a division on the main scale. All the rest are out of line. The number of this division gives the final figure for the correct reading. Suppose, for example, that only the 4 on the vernier scale is exactly aligned with a division on the main scale. Then, if the zero lies between 7 and 8, the correct reading is 7.4. Sometimes, none of the divisions lines up exactly. In that case, the division that is nearest to a division on the main scale is taken as the answer. Vernier

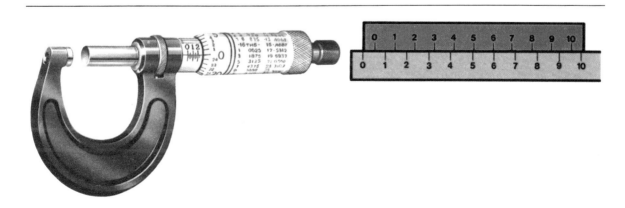

The human body is supported on a column of vertebrae which also serves to protect the spinal cord. The vertebrae are separated by disks of cartilage.

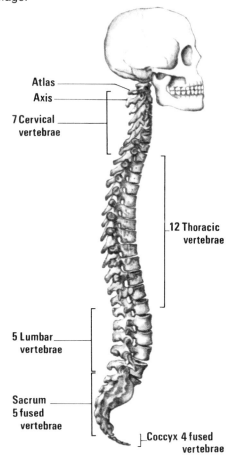

Atlas
Axis
7 Cervical vertebrae
12 Thoracic vertebrae
5 Lumbar vertebrae
Sacrum 5 fused vertebrae
Coccyx 4 fused vertebrae

Vertebrates all have certain characteristics in common. This is illustrated in the "generalized vertebrate" shown here. In the adult stages of most higher vertebrates, some of these characteristics disappear. For example, the pharynx of a mammal does not have gill slits and the nephric duct has disappeared.

scales are used in micrometers for measuring length. (*See* MICROMETER.)   M.E./A.I.

VERTEBRA (vərt′ ə brə) A vertebra is one of the bones that make up the backbone, or spinal column. Two or more of these bones are called vertebrae. All living things with vertebrae are called vertebrates.

A vertebra has a central body with a bony part on each side. The bony part is called a pedicle. The pedicles of each vertebra join to form an arch. This arch serves to protect the spinal cord. It also encloses the opening through which the spinal cord passes. (*See* SKELETON; SPINAL CORD.)

Vertebrae help to attach muscles and ribs to the body. There are small cushions (pads of cartilage) between each vertebra to allow for bending and movement.

A child has 33 vertebrae. Several of these vertebrae unite later in life. An adult has 26 vertebrae.   J.J.A./J.J.F.

VERTEBRATE (vərt′ ə brət) A vertebrate is an animal with a backbone and a cranium (brain case). Vertebrates form most of the phylum Chordata. (*See* CHORDATA.) There are five main groups of vertebrates: fishes, amphibians, reptiles, birds, and mammals. All of them evolved from some fishlike ancestor which probably made its first appearance about 500 million years ago.

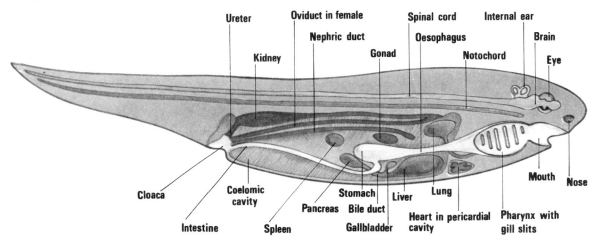

Ureter
Oviduct in female
Nephric duct
Kidney
Gonad
Spinal cord
Oesophagus
Internal ear
Brain
Notochord
Eye
Cloaca
Coelomic cavity
Stomach
Pancreas   Bile duct
Liver
Lung
Mouth
Nose
Intestine
Spleen
Gallbladder
Heart in pericardial cavity
Pharynx with gill slits

Some vertebrates do not possess true bones. Sharks and several other groups of fishes have skeletons made of cartilage. *See also* INVERTEBRATE; SKELETON.

W.R.P./R.J.B.

VESTIGIAL ORGAN (ve stij' əl òr' gən) A vestigial organ is any structure that once was needed by the body but is no longer important. Through evolution it has become small in size. (*See* ADAPTATION.) In human beings, for example, the coccyx is a vestigial tail and the appendix is a vestigial part of the intestines. Sometimes, an important structure is reduced in size in an individual organism. This is usually the result of a mutation and is not a true vestigial organ. (*See* MUTATION.) *See also* EVOLUTION. A.J.C./E.R.L.

VETCH (vech) The vetches are about 150 species of herbaceous plants that belong to the genus *Vicia* of the pea family. They are climb-ing or trailing plants with tendrils and com-pound leaves. (*See* CLIMBING PLANT.) They range in height from 30 to 120 cm [1 to 4 ft]. Blue, white, or yellow flowers are followed by legumes (pods) containing several seeds. Like other members of the pea family, they have nitrogen-fixing bacteria in their roots. (*See* NITROGEN FIXATION.) *See also* PEA FAM-ILY. A.J.C./M.H.S.

VETERINARY MEDICINE (vet' ə rən er ē med' ə sən) Veterinary medicine is a branch of medicine that deals with the health and diseases of animals. Animal doctors are called veterinarians. Veterinarians perform many services, from setting a dog's broken leg to pulling a gorilla's decaying teeth. They play an important role in the control of animal diseases, such as rabies, brucellosis, parrot fever, rabbit fever, and tuberculosis. These

Veterinary surgeons sometimes have to treat very large animals, such as this elephant in the zoo.

diseases can all be transmitted to man from animals. They are called zoonoses.

Veterinarians often work in animal hospitals, which contain equipment similar to that used in hospitals for human beings. Veterinarians are also extremely important to growers of cattle and other livestock. They work to prevent epidemics of disease that can wipe out entire herds. Zoos and circuses also need the services of veterinarians.

There are 18 colleges in the United States that give a degree in veterinary medicine. The degree is called Doctor of Veterinary Medicine (D.V.M. or V.M.D.). Veterinarians must be licensed to practice.

W.R.P./J.J.F.

VIBURNUM (vī bər′ nəm) *Viburnum* is a genus of 200 shrubs and small trees in the honeysuckle family. They grow throughout the world in temperate and subtropical areas. They have simple, opposite leaves which may be toothed or lobed. (*See* LEAF.) The white or pink flowers grow in clusters and may be fertile or sterile. Fertile flowers are bell-shaped, while sterile flowers have spreading petals and no stamens or pistils. The sterile flowers usually grow around the edges of a cluster of fertile flowers. *See also* HONEYSUCKLE FAMILY. A.J.C./M.H.S.

VIDEODISK (vid′ ē ō disk′) A videodisk is a device on which sound and pictures are recorded, and which is played through a television set. The pictures are recorded in color but can be played through either a black-and-white or a color television set. A basic system consists of a videodisk player, a television set, and the disks themselves.

One kind of a videodisk looks like a smooth, shiny metallic phonograph record and is about the same size. However, it has no grooves. Instead, the disk has microscopic ''pits.'' The pits contain codes for both the sound and the picture signals. Each side of the disk can play for thirty minutes.

There are two main kinds of disk systems—contact and optical. In a contact system, a stylus-electrode moves along the surface of the disk. The stylus reads variations in electrical charge in the pits. It transforms the variations into sound and television signals.

The videodisk on this videodisk player can record more than 100,000 book pages.

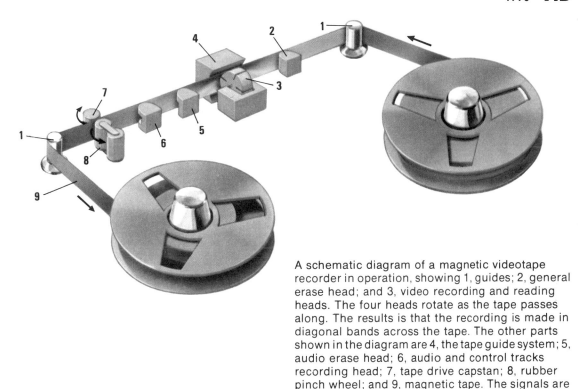

A schematic diagram of a magnetic videotape recorder in operation, showing 1, guides; 2, general erase head; and 3, video recording and reading heads. The four heads rotate as the tape passes along. The results is that the recording is made in diagonal bands across the tape. The other parts shown in the diagram are 4, the tape guide system; 5, audio erase head; 6, audio and control tracks recording head; 7, tape drive capstan; 8, rubber pinch wheel; and 9, magnetic tape. The signals are recorded onto different parts of the tape.

In an optical system, a laser reads patterns of light, which are changed into sound and television signals. Since only the laser beam touches the disk, the disk will never wear out. Optical videodisks are covered with a thin layer of clear plastic, which keeps them clean. This kind of disk is not affected by dust, fingerprints, or scratches.

There are videodisks for thousands of movies, concerts, and educational programs. Disks can also be used, for example, by automobile mechanics to view complicated repair procedures. Or doctors can study operations before performing surgery. The disks can be played in slow or fast motion. They can also repeat sections or be stopped to examine one frame.

Videodisks can also be used to record book pages or photographs. One disk can record 108,000 book pages. *See also* COMPUTER; HI-FI; LASER.   D.A.T./G.D.B.

VIDEOTAPE RECORDING (vid′ ē ō tāp′ ri kȯrd′ ing) A tape recorder is a machine that can record and play back sound. A videotape recorder is similar to an ordinary tape recorder, but it records and plays back both sound and pictures. It can be used to record television programs, for example. A videotape recorder (VTR) works in a way similar to an ordinary tape recorder. (*See* TAPE RECORDER.) A television camera changes an image of a scene into electrical signals. At the same time, a microphone changes the sound into electrical signals. These signals are then fed into the recorder. The VTR contains recording heads that convert the signals into varying magnetic fields. As a strip of magnetic tape is fed past these heads, they produce magnetic patterns on the tape. This tape can then be used to reproduce the original sound and images.

The sound and picture signals are kept

separate in the recorder and are recorded onto different parts of the tape. Usually, the sound signal is recorded onto a narrow track at the top of the tape. The image signal is recorded onto a wider track in the middle of the tape. A control signal is recorded along the bottom of the tape. The tape itself is wider than that used in ordinary tape recorders because it carries the videotrack as well as the soundtrack. Recorders for use at home, called videocassette recorders (VCRs), generally use half-inch tape. Television studios generally use two-inch-wide tape.

The head that records the image signal rotates as the tape passes by it. As a result, the recording is made in diagonal bands across the tape. This allows more information to be stored on a given length of tape. *See also* RECORDING, SOUND.   M.E./A.I.

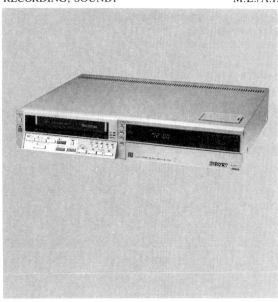

This videocassette recorder (VCR) records programs directly from a television set.

VILLI (vil′ī) Villi are tiny projections that look like fingers on the inner surface of the small intestine. Villi increase the surface of the intestine so that absorption of digested food can take place quickly. Each villus has its own blood supply and a lacteal. The blood collects the food materials and transports

them to the liver. The lacteal, which is filled with lymph, collects fats and transports them to the lymphatic system. (*See* LYMPHATIC SYSTEM.) *See also* INTESTINE.   W.R.P./J.J.F.

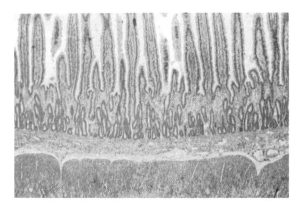

Above, a magnified cross section of a part of the small intestine, showing the villi, tiny fingerlike projections on the inner surface of the intestine. Villi greatly increase the surface area of the intestine, so that the digested food will be absorbed quickly.

VINCI, LEONARDO DA (1452–1519) Leonardo da Vinci (vēn′ chē) was an Italian artist. His paintings and sculptures are famous. He studied anatomy—the body and its parts—to help him with his art. He dissected (cut up) and drew human bodies as well as those of horses. His drawings are very accurate. He observed and drew certain parts of the body that people did not yet understand. But his wonderful powers of observation helped him draw exactly what was there. His drawings also show his skill in dissection and analysis of the human body.

Leonardo also made drawings of amazing machines. At a time when people had only horses and sailboats to help them move from place to place, he made plans for flying machines. He even experimented with building these machines. He also drew plans for diving bells, underground canals, and war machinery.

Facing right, some of Leonardo da Vinci's design for a helicopter.

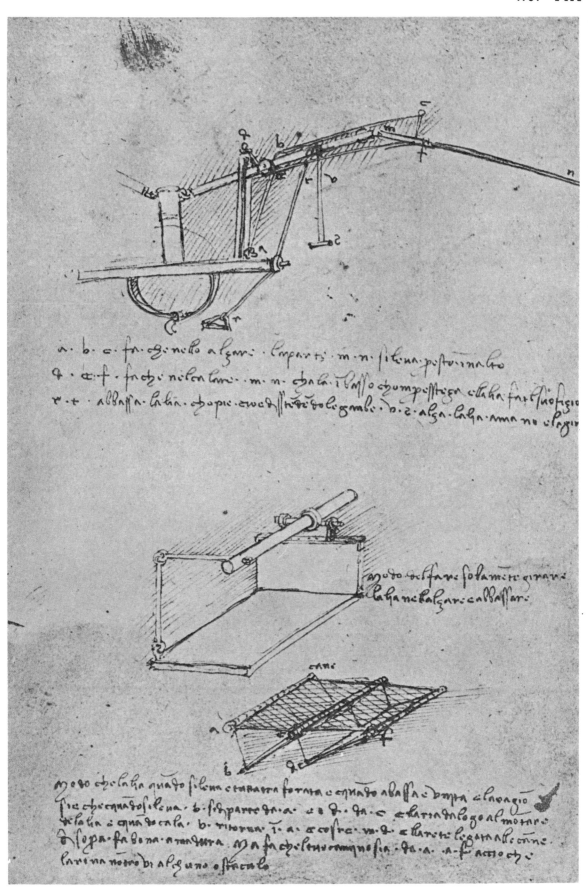

But Leonardo da Vinci did not really have much to do with the growth of technology. Very few people knew of his inventions. It is only because he carefully kept all his drawings that we know he had such ideas.

C.M./D.G.F.

VINE FAMILY The vine (vīn), or grape, family includes 12 genera and 700 species of woody climbing plants. (*See* CLIMBING PLANT.) They are dicotyledons with alternate leaves and clusters of flowers. Most species produce tendrils. Grapes, the most important members of this family, belong to genus *Vitis*.

A.J.C./M.H.S.

VINYL (vīn′ əl) Vinyl describes a group of atoms that are found in a number of organic compounds. The formula for the vinyl group is $CH_2{=}CH-$. Two examples of vinyl compounds are vinyl chloride ($CH_2{=}CHCl$) and vinyl acetate ($CH_3COOCH{=}CH_2$). Mole-

cules of these compounds can be made to link together to form long chain-like molecules. This process is called polymerization. (*See* POLYMERIZATION.) The resulting compounds are called polyvinyl chloride, or PVC, and polyvinyl acetate or PVA. Both PVC and PVA are very useful plastics.

M.E./J.D.

VIOLETS AND PANSIES There are about 500 species of violets (vī′ ə ləts) and pansies (pan′ zēs), all of which belong to the genus *Viola*. They are dicotyledonous herbaceous plants that grow throughout the world. (*See* DICOTYLEDON.) Many varieties produce a rosette of leaves and many flower stalks, each of which bears one blue, purple, yellow, or white flower. Some species have leafy stems with flowers in the axils. Some species produce showy, sterile flowers in the spring, and small, closed, self-fertilizing flowers in the summer. Pansies are really hybrid violets. (*See* HYBRID.) Their petals are often multicolored.

A.J.C./M.H.S.

The great vine at Hampton Court, England, is one of the largest single cultivated vines in existence.

Above, pansies.

Above, violets.

VIPER (vī′ pər) A viper is any of a number of poisonous snakes belonging to the true viper family or the pit viper family. Pit vipers are different from true vipers in that they have a deep pit between the eye and nostril. (*See* PIT VIPER.) True vipers are found in Africa, Europe, India, and Asia. Many pit vipers are found in America. About half of all vipers are pit vipers.

Vipers have two long, hollow fangs in the upper jaw. These fangs carry poison, which is formed in special glands, into the victim's body. It is hard to tell most vipers from other kinds of snakes by head shape or the shape of the neck. Most vipers have thick bodies and short tails. Most true vipers do not lay eggs but bring forth live young. *See also* ADDER; RATTLESNAKE; SNAKE.   J.J.A./R.L.L.

VIREO (vir′ ē ō′) A vireo is a small bird of the family Vireonidae. It is dull-colored, with a gray, brown, or olive back and wings and a white or yellow belly. Its bill is relatively thick with a tiny hook at the end. A vireo is 10 to 15 cm [4 to 6 in] in size. It feeds on insects. The family comprises about 40 species, of which 12 are found throughout North America. Many are common songbirds.

S.R.G./L.L.S.

VIRGINIA CREEPER Virginia creeper (*Parthenocissus quinquefolia*) is a tall climbing plant in the vine family. Sometimes called American ivy or woodbine, it grows throughout the United States. Although similar to poison ivy, the leaves of the plant have five, not three, leaflets that turn red in the fall.

The Virginia creeper climbs by means of tendrils. Each tendril branches into several smaller tendrils. Each of the smaller tendrils ends in a disklike sucker pad which attaches to an object as the plant grows. *See also* VINE FAMILY.   A.J.C./M.H.S.

VIRGO Virgo is the constellation in the zodiac between Leo and Libra. It is visible from the mid-northern hemisphere between March and July. Virgo contains the first magnitude star Spica. Spica is also the brightest star in the constellation. The autumnal equinox, which marks the start of fall in the northern hemisphere, occurs in Virgo.

According to ancient myths, Virgo represents the Roman goddess of justice, Astraea. *See also* CONSTELLATION; EQUINOX; ZODIAC.

J.M.C./C.R.

VIRUS (vī′ rəs) A virus is a microscopic organism that lives in a cell of another living thing. Viruses can be seen only with an electron microscope. They range in size from about 0.01 to 0.3 micron. (1 micron equals 0.001 mm, or 0.000039 in.) Viruses are a major cause of disease. Recently discovered particles called viroids and prions, which are even smaller than viruses, have also been found to cause disease. (*See* MICROBIOLOGY.)

A virus particle consists of protein and nucleic acid, either RNA or DNA. Viruses consisting of RNA are called retroviruses. By itself, a virus is lifeless and cannot reproduce. But inside a living cell, a virus becomes an active organism that can multiply hundreds of times. Thus, unlike bacteria, viruses cannot be grown in a nonliving culture medium, but must be bred in the laboratory on living tissue.

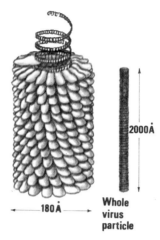

Some viruses have a rodlike shape, shown here. This diagram shows clearly how rodlike viruses are built from protein units, which enclose a spiral molecule of a nucleic acid.

Virus diseases Both plants and animals are attacked by viruses. In most cases, the diseases can occur only in certain creatures or group of creatures. For example, fowl pest, swine fever, and distemper are virus diseases of animals that human beings cannot catch. But cowpox, rabies, and psittacosis (a disease of birds) can be passed on to human beings. Among the many other human virus diseases are the common cold, influenza, polio, chickenpox, smallpox, mumps, measles, shingles, and hepatitis. Some kinds of cancer such as leukemia are caused by viruses. The virus HTLV-III causes AIDS (acquired immune deficiency syndrome). Some viruses destroy crops, and viruses known as bacteriophages attack bacteria. (*See* BACTERIOPHAGE.)

There is very little doctors can do to treat virus diseases directly. They can treat the effects of the disease and any complications that may arise, and in many cases prevent a disease. But few drugs have been discovered that really work against viruses in the way that antibiotics and sulfa drugs fight bacteria. A person's body does, however, fight against invading viruses in two ways. It produces antibodies which make the virus particles clump together so that they can be destroyed. Also, the body produces a substance called interferon. Interferon helps keep viruses from spreading from cell to cell. (*See* IMMUNITY; INTERFERON.) A technique has been recently

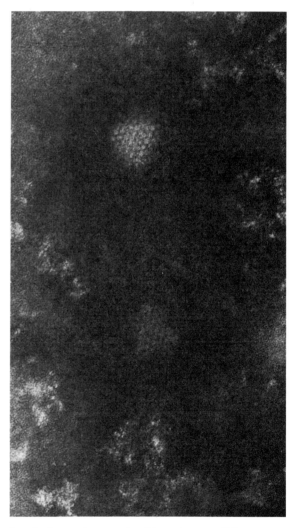

An electron micrograph of two virus particles having a polyhedral shape with many facets. Each facet is a protein unit and the whole protein polyhedron encloses a nucleic acid molecule.

developed for producing interferon artificially by cloning genetic material. (*See* CLONE; GENETICS.) Now, with larger quantities of the substance to work with, researchers have a better chance of finding ways to treat virus disease directly.

Currently, the only way to prevent virus disease is by use of vaccines. Vaccination depends on the body's ability to produce antibodies. Once a person has had a virus disease, his or her body always retains some ability to form the correct antibodies. Thus, such diseases may attack a person only once. By placing dead or weakened viruses in a person, a doctor can give him or her artificial immunity to a virus disease.

Virologists are scientists who study viruses, chiefly to learn how the organisms cause disease and how to control these organisms. Scientists also use viruses for such purposes as insect control, cell research, and development of vaccines.   J.J.A./J.J.F.

VISCOSITY (vis käs′ ət ē) Viscosity is the resistance of a liquid or a gas to an object moving through it. If a stone is dropped into water, it sinks fairly quickly. The same stone would sink much more slowly in oil, however, because oil is more viscous than water. The greater the viscosity of a substance, the more it resists an object moving in it. When an object falls through a liquid or a gas, it eventually reaches a maximum speed. This speed is called its terminal velocity. (*See* TERMINAL VELOCITY.) The more viscous the liquid or gas, the lower the terminal velocity of an object moving through it. Viscosity also affects the rate at which a liquid can be poured. Water can be poured more quickly than can oil. This is because water is less viscous.

To understand viscosity, think of a liquid or gas as being made up of thin layers. Viscosity is caused by friction between these layers. An object falling through a liquid or gas is slowed down by friction between it and the liquid or gas.

The viscosity of a liquid decreases as its temperature increases. The viscosity of a gas, however, increases as its temperature increases.   M.E./J.D.

VITAMIN (vīt′ ə mən) Vitamins are complex chemical substances found in many foods. The human body needs them for health and growth. The body makes some vitamins, but usually in amounts too small to meet its needs. Other vitamins are not made in the body. These must be supplied. No one knows exactly how all vitamins work. Doctors do know that vitamins have very special uses. One vitamin therefore cannot take the place of another. The steady absence of one vitamin in an otherwise complete diet causes a deficiency disease. (*See* DISEASE.) Rickets, scurvy, and pellagra are examples of deficiency diseases.

It is best to obtain vitamins by eating the foods in which they occur. There are also pills that contain a single vitamin or a combination of vitamins. People should consult their doctor before they take any vitamin pills.

Scientists have discovered about 25 vitamins and their different forms that are very important to human beings and other forms of life. Experts believe that there are many more vitamins to be discovered.

There are two basic groups of vitamins. One group of vitamins dissolves in fat and is therefore called the "fat-soluble" group. Vitamins A, D, E, and K are in this group. The other group is known as "water-soluble" vitamins. These vitamins, understandably, dissolve in water. Among this group are vitamin C and the B group of vitamins.

Vitamin A aids the building and growth of body cells. This vitamin is therefore vital for the growth of children and for good development of babies before birth. Vitamin A is also important for good vision at night. (*See* EYE AND VISION.) Vitamin B_1 is also called thiamine. This vitamin prevents and cures

BERIBERI.) Vitamin B₂, called riboflavin, is needed for growth, healthy skin, and for the eyes. Vitamin C, or ascorbic acid, prevents and cures scurvy. (*See* SCURVY.)

Vitamin D is a group of 10 vitamins that prevents rickets. (*See* RICKETTSIA.) Scientists believe that vitamin D₃ forms in the skin when the body is exposed to sunlight. Because of this, it is called the "sunshine vitamin." A lack of vitamin D may lead to bone damage; too much may cause kidney disease.

All of the functions of vitamin E, also called tocopherol, are not known. It is necessary for reproduction in animals. Vitamin K is necessary for making the blood clot.

The more that is learned about vitamins, the more it is realized how these chemical substances play a part in all aspects of human activity. J.J.A./J.J.F.

VOLATILE LIQUID (väl′ əl əl lik′ wəd) If a liquid is left uncovered, it tends to evaporate. This is because molecules leave the liquid and escape into the air. These molecules make up what is known as the vapor. (*See* VAPOR.) The vapor is a gas and, like all gases, it exerts a pressure. As the temperature of the liquid increases, more molecules escape and the vapor pressure increases. Eventually, at a certain temperature, the vapor pressure equals the atmospheric pressure and the liquid boils. A volatile liquid is one that has a high vapor pressure at normal temperatures. Therefore it evaporates quickly and its boiling point is not much higher than normal temperature. When a liquid evaporates, it draws heat from its surroundings. Volatile liquid are used for cooling surfaces. For example, chloroethane (ethyl chloride) is a very volatile liquid. Its boiling point is 12.5°C [54.5°F]. When it is sprayed onto skin, it evaporates quickly. This cools the skin enough to deaden, or anesthetize, it. Chloroethane is used as a local anesthetic, or pain killer. (*See* ANESTHETIC.) *See also* BOILING POINT. M.E./J.D.

VOLCANO

A volcano (väl kā′ nō) is a vent, or opening, in the earth's surface through which lava, gases, and rocks burst forth. A volcano also refers to the mountain or hill that forms around the vent.

Volcanoes have been discovered on Venus and Mars and on Io, one of the moons of Jupiter. Photographs of Io transmitted to earth by *Voyager* spacecraft clearly show one of its volcanoes erupting, the first such extraterrestrial eruption ever recorded.

Formation of a volcano Geologists do not completely understand what causes volcanoes. Most scientists believe that great heat and pressure beneath the earth's surface cause rocks to melt, forming magma. The melting rocks release gas which mixes with the magma. The magma formation process probably occurs about 80 to 160 km [50 to 100 mi] below the surface.

Magma is lighter than solid rock. As a result, the magma rises toward the surface. As the magma rises, it melts the rocks along the way. The magma rises until it is as close as 3 km [2 mi] below the surface. The magma then forms a large reservoir called a magma chamber.

The magma in the chamber is under great pressure from the rocks above it. Eventually, the pressure causes the magma to melt a channel through a weak point in the surrounding rock. As the magma nears the surface, it releases its gases. This causes the magma and gases to explode through the surface. The opening that the magma erupts from is called the central vent. Magma flows from the chamber through the channel and out the vent. The magma, or lava, hardens around the vent, building up a volcanic mountain. Sometimes, magma melts smaller channels through the side of the mountain, and thus flows out from a secondary vent.

Volcanic material   The three main materials vomited from a volcano are lava, gases, and pyroclastic rocks.

Lava is magma above the earth's surface. Newly erupted lava may have a temperature of 1,100°C [2,012°F]. Lava is often classified according to its thickness. Very fluid lava quickly flows down from the vent. When it cools it forms a smooth rock called pahoehoe. Thicker lava cools to form jagged rocks called aa. Lava may also harden into tunnels, tubes, and other interesting forms.

Gas belches out of an erupting volcano like smoke out of a chimney. Often, steam is formed from the heating of ground water. The gas usually looks like black smoke.

Volcanoes also throw out many pyroclastic rocks. They include volcanic dust, ash, and bombs. These rocks are often thrown high into the air during an eruption.

Volcanic dust is made up of tiny particles with diameters less than 0.25 mm [0.01 in]. This dust may be carried by the wind around the world, causing spectacular red sunsets. Volcanic ash is particles with diameters less than 0.5 cm [0.2 in]. Volcanic ash usually falls directly to the surface. Volcanic ash is one of the most efficient preservers of fossils. (*See* FOSSIL.) Sometimes, the ash mixes with water to form a mudflow. Volcanic bombs are the largest rock fragments that erupt from a volcano.

Kinds of volcanoes   Volcanoes are sometimes distinguished by their shape. Cinder

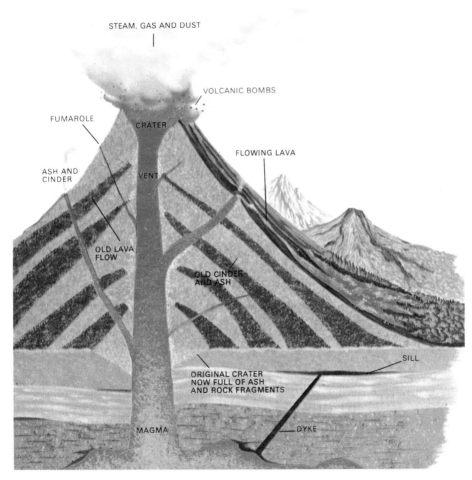

A section through a volcano shows how it is gradually built up by layers of solidified lava and ash from earlier eruptions. Molten magma is forced out through the vent and sometimes through side channels. Where a flow of magma is blocked, it solidifies underground.

Above, some volcanoes erupt with great force, throwing up showers of hot glowing cinders and lava from their vents.

cones are volcanoes with steep sides that are built up by the material laid down around the vent. Paricutin in Mexico is a cinder cone.

Cones called composite contain layers of pyroclastic rocks alternating with layers of lava. Italy's Mount Vesuvius is a composite cone. Shield volcanoes are low, gently sloping volcanoes formed from overlapping lava flows.

Volcanoes are also classified by the amount of their acitivity. Active volcanoes may be erupting or about to erupt, may erupt at fairly regular intervals from weeks to a hundred years or more apart, or may be dormant for many years. An eruption is always possible. An extinct volcano is one that has been completely inactive for very long periods of time. Extinct volcanoes will probably never erupt again.

Volcanology Volcanology is the study of volcanoes. Volcanologists study the origins, eruptions, and locations of volcanoes. There are about 600 active volcanoes in the world. The chief area of volcanic activity is called the "ring of fire." It lies around the Pacific Ocean. Other areas of volcanic activity include the central Mediterranean region, Iceland, the East African rift valley, and Hawaii.

Scientific theories and observations since the sixteenth century helped to form the currently held theory of volcanoes. Since the middle of the 1960s, geologists and other scientists have used the theory of plate tectonics to explain volcanic activity.

Plate tectonics proposes that the earth's crust is made up of about 20 plates which are constantly, but slowly, moving. When two plates press against each other, one plate usually slides under the other in what is known as a subduction zone. This happens in the Pacific Ocean "ring of fire" area. When plates move apart, a rift zone is formed. This happens in the mid-Atlantic ridge, which goes through Iceland. When the plates pull apart in the rift zones, magma bubbles up in order to patch the rift. This would explain the less violent flows of lava characteristic of Icelandic and Hawaiian volcanoes.

Certain things happen before an eruption in subduction zones. Signs include a rise in temperature close to the volcano, gases coming from the vent, and earth tremors or low-level earthquakes. An increase in silica content in the caldera of a volcano is also a sign of an approaching eruption. An instrument called a tiltmeter is used to measure changes in the contours of a volcanic mountain. Today, volcanologists can even identify volcanic "hot spots" appearing on photographs made by weather satellites.

Even though forecasting volcanic eruptions is not perfected, scientists have been more and more successful. The weather satellite *Nimbus II* produced data about the volcanic island Surtsey, near Iceland, a day before it erupted into existence. In 1980, scientists knew in advance that an eruption was imminent in the 40,000-year-old Mount Saint Helens in Washington's Cascade Mountains. Countless lives were saved because people had been evacuated from the area before the eruption.

The eruption of Mount Saint Helens may have been the most closely and scientifically studied violent eruption of all time. Photographs, measurements, and tests verified many long-held theories. They will undoubtedly be useful in future forecasting.

The high cost of equipment, the scarcity of trained volcanologists, and the wide geographic scattering of potentially eruptive volcanoes compound the problem of forecasting. The study of volcanoes is a long-term affair. An active volcano may go a hundred years or more between eruptions, and few governments or scholars have the funds or manpower to monitor all possible sites.

Volcanoes do serve useful purposes. They allow the release of energy that builds

This aerial view shows huge amounts of steam and ash rising from Mount Saint Helens (Washington) during an eruption in 1980.

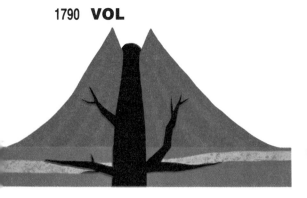

In a dead volcano, the cone may be eroded away, leaving only the neck or plug, which resists erosion much longer.

up between the earth's moving plates. They also provide extremely fertile soil. People in Iceland heat their homes with water from volcanic springs. (*See also* LAVA; MAGMA; MOUNTAIN.) J.M.C./W.R.S.

VOLE (vōl) The vole is a small, stout rodent with short legs and tiny ears. Voles have a body length of about 13 cm [5 in]. Most voles have gray fur. Voles are often named for the places in which they live. Meadow voles are commonly found in North America. The most common type of meadow vole, *Microtus pennsylvanicus,* is found in the north central and northeastern United States. Voles may live in grassy fields or swampy plains. Some types live near water. Others live in bogs, wooded areas, or rocky, mountainous areas. Voles feed on grass, roots, and seeds.

Voles are close relatives of lemmings. (*See* LEMMING.) Voles have been responsible for damaging huge areas of meadow land in the United States. J.J.A./J.J.M.

VOLT (vōlt) The volt is an electrical unit. It measures the potential difference between two points. (*See* POTENTIAL.) Suppose that two points are at different electrical potentials. Then work has to be done to move an electric charge from one point to the other. If the size of the charge is one coulomb and the work done on it is one joule, then the potential difference between the two points is one volt.

Small voltages are measured by instruments called potentiometers. They can measure voltages as small as a millionth of a volt. Larger voltages are measured by galvanometers. (*See* GALVANOMETER.) The volt is named after the Italian physicist Alessandro Volta. (*See* VOLTA, ALESSANDRO.) *See also* JOULE. M.E./J.D.

VOLTA, ALESSANDRO (1745–1827)
Alessandro Volta (vōl' tä) was an Italian physicist. He was born at Como, in Lombardy. He became interested in electricity when he was quite young and later taught physics at Como high school. While he was there, he invented a machine called an electrophorus. This is used for building up a strong charge of static electricity. It is, in fact, the basis of the capacitors, devices to store electricity, in use today. (*See* CAPACITOR AND CAPACITANCE.)

Volta's electrophorus made him famous. He became a university professor and continued his work with electricity. His most famous achievement was the invention of the electric battery. This invention came out of his work on Luigi Galvani's discoveries. Volta believed the electric current Galvani got from connecting two metal wires to a frog's leg muscle came from the metals. He proved this was true and went on to make a current from two metal (copper and zinc) plates in a salt solution. He improved this design to make what is called a voltaic pile. In 1801, he was invited to show this invention to the Emperor Napoleon III. He was awarded many honors and medals for his work. The unit of electromotive force and potential difference, the volt, is named after him. *See also* BATTERY; CONDENSER. C.M./D.G.F.

Alessandro Volta

VOLTAGE REGULATOR (vōl′ tij reg′ yə lāt′ ər) Many electrical devices, such as radio receivers and electric motors, need an exact voltage to work properly. To keep the voltage at the desired value, these devices contain a voltage regulator. Some voltage regulators work automatically. Others are operated by hand. An example of the automatic type is the thermistor. (*See* THERMISTOR.) If the voltage across a thermistor varies, then its electrical resistance changes. The change in resistance opposes the change in voltage and corrects it. Hand-operated voltage regulators also use a varying resistance. M.E./J.D.

VOLTMETER (vōlt′ mēt′ ər) A voltmeter is an instrument that is used to measure the potential difference, or voltage, between two points. Most voltmeters are made up of an instrument called an ammeter with a high resistance in series. (*See* AMMETER.) An ammeter measures electric current. When a voltage is applied across the voltmeter, a very small current flows through it because of the high resistance. This allows the voltage to be measured. M.E./A.I.

VOLUME (väl′ yəm) Volume is a measure of space. The space can contain air or be a vacuum inside a container. The space can also be filled with a liquid or solid. Volume is measured in cubic centimeters and cubic meters or cubic inches and cubic feet.

The volume of a rectangular container, such as a box, is found by multiplying the length by the width by the depth. A cubic foot equals 1,728 cubic inches, and a cubic meter equals one million cubic centimeters.

The volume of a cylinder is found by multiplying the area of the base by the height. The area of the base is found by multiplying π (pi—about 3.1416) by the square of the radius.

The volume of liquids is measured in units such as milliliters, liters, gallons, quarts, pints, and fluid ounces. W.R.P./J.T.

VOLVOX (väl′ väks′) Volvox is a one-celled, chlorophyll-containing, flagellated organism. Most scientists classify volvox in

Below, a photomicrograph of volvox colonies containing daughter colonies.

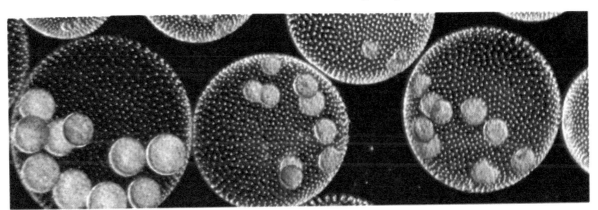

the kingdom Protista, but others consider it to be either a plant or an animal. Since it contains chlorophyll, volvox is able to produce its own food by photosynthesis. Since it has a flagellum, volvox is able to move about under its own power.

Volvox usually live in ball-shaped colonies of as many as 60,000 cells. As these cells wave their flagella, the colony rolls through the water. Some colonies produce smaller daughter colonies which may break away from the parent colony. These daughter colonies then form new colonies of their own. Some colonies produce male and female gametes. These gametes combine to form a zygote which stays in the parent colony. When the parent colony dies, these zygotes are released and can form new colonies. The zygotes are thick-walled and can survive unfavorable environmental conditions. *See also* PROTOZOA. A.J.C./E.R.L.

VULCANIZING (vəl′ kə nīz′ ing) Vulcanizing is the process of treating rubber to give it useful properties. In its natural state, rubber tends to become soft and sticky in warm weather. In cold weather, it tends to become brittle and crack. Scientists tried to remove these undesirable properties. This was finally achieved by an American inventor, Charles Goodyear, in 1838. He discovered that the properties of rubber were improved if sulfur were added and the mixture heated. This process is called vulcanization. Vulcanized rubber is much tougher than natural rubber and can be used for many more purposes. The molecules of rubber are like very long chains. It is thought that during vulcanization these chains are linked up to each other by the sulfur atoms. This prevents the molecules from sliding past each other and the rubber becomes hard. M.E./J.D.

VULTURE (vəl′ chər) A vulture is a large bird found in America that belongs to the family Cathartidae. It is related to the hawk, eagle, and falcon. The vulture is mostly black, with patches of white on its wings and a naked head (without feathers). The bill of a vulture is stocky and the talons (claws) are

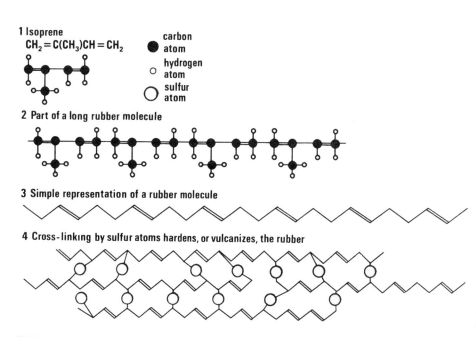

These diagrams show how sulfur is used in vulcanizing rubber. 1. Natural rubber is made up of molecules of a substance called isoprene. 2. In rubber, these molecules are joined together to form long chainlike molecules that can slide over each other. This is why rubber stretches easily. 3. The long molecules can be represented like this. 4. In vulcanization, sulfur is added to the rubber. The sulfur links the molecules together. The molecules can no longer slide over each other. The rubber is now hard and springy and will not stretch easily.

A royal vulture.

A lappet-faced vulture.

A white-hood vulture scavenges the carcass of a buffalo.

and southeastern United States. The California condor, the largest bird in North America, reaches lengths of 112.5 cm [45 in] and may have a wingspan of 300 cm [120 in]. It is nearly extinct, with fewer than 50 remaining birds, all of which live in a small area in California. (*See* CONDOR.) *See also* HAWK.

S.R.G./L.L.S.

very powerful. A vulture eats dead animals, and the bill and talons are used to tear the flesh off the bones. Very rarely, a vulture will kill and then eat an animal.

There are three species of vultures in North America. Other vultures are found in Europe. They are related to hawks, however, and not to American vultures. The turkey vulture grows to lengths of 62.5 cm [25 in] with a wingspan of 180 cm [72 in]. It is found throughout most of the United States, Central, and South America. The slightly smaller black vulture lives in the American tropics

WADER (wād′ ər) Wader, or shorebird, is a general term for a long-legged bird that spends much of its time in the shallow waters of marshes and seashores. Most waders also have long beaks with which they probe into the mud in search of worms and other small animals. Waders belong to several families, the largest of which is Scolopacidae. Its members include sandpipers, curlews, snipe, woodcock, redshank, and ruff. Most waders nest far inland and migrate to the coasts in winter. Other well known waders are the avocet, oyster catcher, and turnstone. The oyster catcher inserts its long, bladelike beak into

Wader is a general term for many birds that are found at the shore. Although classified as a wader, this wattled plover actually lives on dry land.

Above, the pied stilt is a typical wader. It has long legs for walking along the wet shore and a long beak which it uses to probe for its food by the shore.

Above, this fishing heron might be regarded as a typical wader, but in fact herons are not classified by ornithologists as waders; they are more closely related to the storks.

a partly open bivalve (such as a clam or oyster) and scoops the animal from its shell.

W.R.P./L.L.S.

WAKSMAN, SELMAN ABRAHAM (1888–1973) Selman Waksman (wäks′ mən) was a Russian-American microbiologist. He was born at Priluki in Russia and became an American citizen in 1916. Waksman was at Rutgers University in 1939 when René Dubos discovered a soil microbe that could kill bacteria. Work was already under way to isolate penicillin. (*See* FLEMING, SIR ALEXANDER; FLOREY, HOWARD WALTER.) Waksman gave the name "antibiotic" to penicillin and the new agent Dubos discovered. He then set out to find if there were other molds that produced antibiotic substances.

Waksman discovered that a mold of the Streptomycete family could kill germs. He extracted the pure antibiotic from it in 1943 and called it streptomycin. He was awarded the 1952 Nobel Prize for Medicine and Physiology for this work. He gave the prize money to the research fund at Rutgers and continued with his work.   C.M./D.G.F.

WALKINGSTICK (wȯ′ king stik) The walkingsticks, or stick insects, are 2,500 species of insects that belong to the order Phasmatodea. Their bodies look so much like sticks or twigs that these insects can hardly be seen as they eat leaves in trees and shrubs. They are able to grow lost legs or antennae again. (*See* REGENERATION.) Although some species have small wings, they rarely fly. Some species give off a foul-smelling liquid if threatened.

Above, a walkingstick.

Most walkingsticks lay single eggs which fall to the ground. These eggs look like seeds, so most are eaten by hungry animals. In some walkingstick species, there are few, if any, males. Their eggs develop by parthenogenesis. (*See* PARTHENOGENESIS.) Although found throughout the world, most walkingsticks live in the tropics. One tropical species is the longest of all living insects (32 cm [13 in]). *See also* CAMOUFLAGE; INSECT; MIMICRY.   A.J.C./J.E.R.

WALLABY (wäl′ ə bē) The wallaby is a small mammal that looks like a kangaroo and belongs to the group known as marsupials. The animal has long hind legs, small front legs, and a sturdy tail. When sitting in an upright position, the wallaby often uses its tail to lean on. There are many kinds of wallabies. The animals range from 30 to 90 cm [1 to 3 ft] in length, not including the tail. Bush kangaroo is another name for the wallaby.

Wallabies live in various places, from open fields to dense forests. The animals are found in Australia and New Guinea. Some species have become extinct through competition with dogs and other animals introduced by humans. Other types are now endangered from the same cause. *See also* KANGAROO.
      J.J.A./J.J.M.

WALLACE, ALFRED RUSSEL (1823–1913) Alfred Russel Wallace (wȯl′ əs) was a British naturalist. He was born at Usk, in Monmouthshire. He set off as naturalist on an expedition to the Amazon River in South America in 1848. In 1854 he sailed to Malaya and the East Indies, seeing Australia and Asia.

Wallace's work on these travels was to look carefully at the many different creatures he saw. He could see that there were big differences between animals from one area to another. He decided that the world could be divided into six areas, which are now called Wallace's Realms. They are the Palearctic,

Nearctic, Neotropical, Ethiopian, Oriental, and Australasian Regions. It was from this idea that Wallace first began to think about why animals in different places should be different from each other. He wondered why Australian mammals were completely different from the ones in Asia.

Wallace worked out a theory of evolution about the same time as Darwin did. He had worked it out in a completely different way, but both men had seen that natural selection could be the secret. Darwin had done more experiments to prove his theory, while Wallace had a great deal of evidence from all over the world. Both Darwin and Wallace were helped in this work by the population studies of Thomas Malthus.

When he was an old man, Wallace found the idea that humans had descended from apes upsetting. He could not see how a soul could have "evolved." This problem troubled him, and he became a spiritualist. *See also* DARWIN, CHARLES ROBERT; EVOLUTION.

C.M./D.G.F.

WALLEYE (wȯl′ lī′) A walleye is a freshwater fish that belongs to the perch family Percidae. (*See* PERCH.) It is usually a brownish colored fish with a white belly, pointed snout, and many sharp teeth. The walleye averages between 33 to 50 cm [13 to 20 in] in length. It feeds mostly on other fishes, although young walleyes eat insects. The species is found from southeastern United States north to the Arctic Circle. It is the most common fish in some parts of central Canada.

The walleye is a very popular game fish, especially in Canada. The flesh is highly prized for food. The fish is called a walleye because its eyes are large and silvery. When the fish dies, the eyes become white.

S.R.G./E.C.M.

WALLFLOWER (wȯl′ flaủr′) The wallflowers are a group of perennial (blooming each year) plants that belong to the genus *Cheiranthus* of the mustard family. The most common species is *Cheiranthus cheiri*, a native of southern Europe. Its woody stems are 30 to 60 cm [1 to 2 ft] long and they may grow along walls or on cliffs for support. This species has alternate, spear-shaped leaves and clusters of fragrant orange or yellow flowers. (*See* LEAF.) *See also* MUSTARD FAMILY.

A.J.C./M.H.S.

WALNUT (wȯl′ nət) The walnut is a tree that bears one of the more popular nuts in the world. The tree belongs to the walnut family (Juglandaceae). Several types of walnut trees grow in the United States. The black walnut and white walnut, or butternut, are native to the eastern part of the country. The English or Persian walnut is grown in California. The wood of Black and English walnut trees is used to make fine furniture.

English walnut trees bear nuts that many people buy. The trees have gray bark, large leaflets, and mild-flavored nuts. All walnuts grow in shells. Black walnut trees are grown mainly for their dark-brown, fine-grained wood, which is used in furniture and gunstocks. Black walnut trees are the largest of the walnuts and often grow 46 m [150 ft] high.

The United States leads the world in the production of walnuts. The area around Stockton, California, is the center of the country's walnut industry. W.R.P./M.H.S.

WALRUS (wȯl′ rəs) The walrus (*Odobenus rosmarus*) is a marine (water) mammal found in the Arctic Ocean, North Atlantic Ocean, and Pacific Ocean. Scientists classify the walrus as a type of large seal. (*See* SEAL.) The walrus is the only seal with tusks. The animal uses its two ivory tusks, which are upper canine teeth, to dig out shellfish, to climb on ice, and also for defense. The tusks may grow as long as 99 cm [39 in]. The animal's four feet are flattened into flippers, thereby making the walrus a good swimmer.

An adult male walrus is larger than the female. Males grow to about 3.7 m [12 ft] in length and weigh up to 1,400 kg [3,000 lb].

The female suckles her baby, called a calf or pup, for about two years. Most walruses live in herds.

Walruses are hunted chiefly for their meat. Eskimos use the hides to make various things, such as small boats. Eskimos also use the oil of the walrus as fuel for heat and light.

J.J.A./J.J.M.

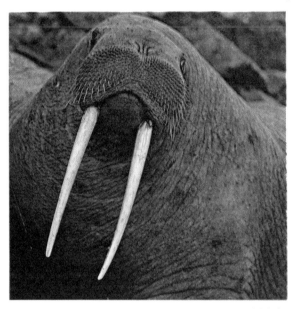

A walrus may have tusks as long as 100 cm [39 in].

WARBLER (wŏr′blər) In the Americas, the warblers are small birds that belong to the family Parulidae. They are named for a large group of birds known as the Old World warblers (family Muscicapidae), but they are not related to them. The New World warblers are usually called wood warblers. They chirp or trill simple, melodious songs. They do not really ''warble'' their songs as do the Old World warblers.

Of the 120 species of wood warblers, 55 live in North America. They feed mostly on insects and nectar and range in length from 10 to 12.5 cm [4 to 5 in]. Most of these warblers migrate, or move, south for the winter, some as far south as South America. (*See* MIGRA-

TION.) They usually migrate at night in large flocks made up of several different species of warblers. Since most of the birds are dull in color at this time, it is often difficult to tell one species from another. By the time they return to their northern nesting areas in the spring, however, the males are usually vividly colored to help them attract mates.

A.J.C./L.L.S.

WARM-BLOODED ANIMAL A warm-blooded, or homeothermic, animal has a relatively constant body temperature, regardless of the temperature around it. Mammals and birds are the only homeothermic animals. In these animals, there is a balance between heat lost and heat produced. This balance is controlled by the hypothalamus, part of the brain. (*See* BRAIN.) Special nerves are constantly sending the hypothalamus information about the temperature throughout the body. Based on these ''status reports,'' the hypothalamus makes the necessary adjustments.

If the body is becoming overheated, for example, the blood flow to the skin increases and perspiration increases. As a result, the body gives off more heat through the skin and cools down. Increased blood flow in the skin may make a person appear flushed, or red-faced. If the body is becoming too cool, blood flow and perspiration decrease, reducing heat loss. Tiny hairs on the skin may stand on end, trapping an insulating layer of air. Since body heat increases with muscular activity, shivering (involuntary muscle contractions) helps keep the body warm.

Each homeothermic animal has its own normal body temperature. This temperature varies during the day. It is also affected by exercise or extremes of hot and cold weather. Some homeothermic animals hibernate. (*See* HIBERNATION.) During this time, an animal's body temperature drops to about the same temperature as its surroundings. *See also* TEMPERATURE, BODY; METABOLISM.

A.J.C./E.R.L.

The spines of the dragon fish (top, facing left) contain poison, and this fish appropriately has warning coloration which discourages would-be attackers. The puss moth caterpillar (bottom, facing left) is an example of an animal that has bright warning coloration without being venomous or poisonous.

WARNING COLORATION (wȯrn′ ing kəl′ ə rā′ shən) Warning coloration is used by a plant or animal to tell enemies that it is dangerous or undesirable. As a result, the enemy leaves the organism alone. An example of warning coloration is the bright pattern of red, black, and yellow colors on a poisonous coral snake. Other animals learn to recognize the snake by its unusual colors, and they stay away. Warning coloration is the opposite of camouflage. (*See* CAMOUFLAGE.) Camouflaged animals protect themselves by blending in with the area around them. An animal that shows warning coloration protects itself by making sure that every animal sees it—and stays away. *See also* MIMICRY; PIGMENTATION; PROTECTIVE COLORATION.

S.R.G./R.J.B.

The gila monster is a venomous lizard with warning coloration which warns other animals to stay away.

WARTHOG (wȯrt′ hȯg′) The warthog (*Phacochoerus aetheopicus*) is a wild African pig that is found from South Africa to Ethiopia. An adult warthog stands about 76 cm [30 in] tall at the shoulder. It has brown or gray skin and a long, coarse mane down the center of its back. The rest of its body has little or no hair. Warthogs of both sexes have tusks that may grow to be 60 cm [2 ft] long. Between their tusks and their eyes, warthogs have ugly bulges, or warts, from which these animals get their name. An adult warthog may weigh 91 kg [200 lb].

Warthogs travel in small groups. The female gives birth to as many as eight young at one time. Warthogs prefer forests and grasslands and live in burrows built by other animals. They eat almost anything that is edible.

If provoked, warthogs usually run away with their tails raised vertically. They may fight hard, however, using their large tusks as weapons.

J.M.C./J.J.M.

Warthogs are named for the unsightly bulges, or warts, on their faces.

WASP (wäsp) The wasp is a stinging insect related to bees and ants. It is the name given to several kinds of insects belonging to the order Hymenoptera, but especially to the familiar yellowjackets and hornets of the family Vespidae. Most wasps have slender bodies with a narrow waist and four wings. The bodies may have different colors. Yellowjackets have black bodies with bands of bright yellow. Other varieties of wasps are steel blue, black, or reddish. The mouths of wasps are fitted for chewing hard objects and lapping up liquids.

Wasps give painful stings. However, they sting only when they are frightened or bothered. Only female and worker wasps have stingers, which are thin, pointed drills hidden in the rear tips of their abdomens. Despite the fact that many persons fear wasps because of their stinging ability, these insects are helpful to humanity. They destroy large numbers of harmful insects and caterpillars.

Wasps often live in colonies like those of bees and ants. The colony is made up of different kinds of wasps, queens (females), males, and workers (females). Each type has a different job to do. Wasps that live together like this are known as social wasps. Other wasps that build separate nests and live alone are known as solitary wasps.

Some social wasps build their nests of wasp paper—a mixture of plant fibers and old wood. They chew this mixture into a pulp, using much saliva. When this pulp dries out, it becomes real paper. Wasps mold this pulp into rows of cells, much like those in a bee honeycomb. The nest itself may be located in several places—under the eaves of a porch roof, attached to a rafter in an attic, or hanging from the limb of a tree or bush.

Unlike bees, a wasp colony lasts only through the summer. Wasps do not store food and most of them die in the fall. A small group of young queens lives through the winter by entering a type of hibernation. (*See* HIBERNATION.) These queens form the new colony the next summer.

Solitary wasps are masons, carpenters, excavators, and diggers. They work for and defend their offspring, but never see them. Potter wasps make dainty nests out of mud and saliva. Stonemaker wasps mix pebbles with the mud and saliva and build nests on the surfaces of rocks in the open. Carpenter wasps tunnel into trees and posts. Earth-mining and digger wasps dig tunnels into the ground.

Female solitary wasps feed their young with caterpillars, spiders, beetles, and flies that they catch and paralyze with their stingers. The female eats only nectar and fruit juices while collecting this food. After putting a large supply of these other insects into the nest, she lays an egg on one of the bodies in each cell, or room, in the nest. Then she seals up the nest and goes away. The larva

hatches in a few days and finds a supply of food. Later, the larva spins a silken cocoon, called a pupa, around itself. It may remain this way through the winter. The full-grown wasp gnaws its way out of the pupa in the spring. *See also* BEE; HORNET.   W.R.P./J.E.R.

Wasps are related to bees and ants.

WATER

Water (wȯt′ ər) is the colorless, tasteless substance that covers about 71 percent of the earth's surface. About 97 percent of the water on earth is in the oceans. Some of this water is evaporated and returned to the land as rain or snow. Water is also found in rivers, lakes, and ponds, as well as underground, and frozen in glaciers and ice sheets, and as water vapor in the atmosphere. There are approximately 1.4 billion cubic km [330 million cubic mi] of water on the earth.

Importance of water Water is necessary for all life on earth. The human body contains about 65 percent water. Although most people can live a month or longer with no food, a person will die after seven to ten days without any water. It is estimated that each American uses about 380 liters [100 gallons] of water daily. Most drinking water must be purified before use. (*See* WATER SUPPLY.)

Plants depend on water for growth. Water

Water is perhaps the world's most important natural resource.

dissolves minerals and other nutrients in the ground. The roots of plants draw this nutritious water from the soil.

Farmers depend on water for their crops. In an area of sufficient rainfall, the securing of water presents no problem. In arid regions, however, water must be transported from a water source to the needy area. This process is called irrigation. (*See* IRRIGATION.) People usually settle near rivers, lakes, or other fresh water sources. The ancient Egyptian and Mesopotamian civilizations were centered in river valleys.

Water is important for industry. Its main function is for cooling. For example, some industries use dangerous chemical reactions that produce large amounts of heat needed to make a product. Water is often used to keep the reaction under control by cooling the containers or other apparatus. Other industrial applications of water include cleaning and air

Some parts of the earth are almost completely waterless, but people have found ways of carrying water to them, as is shown in this photograph of a desert canal, above.

conditioning, and even as a raw material in such things as soft drinks and alcoholic beverages. Unfortunately, many industries dump their waste water into rivers or lakes, thus polluting the clean water. (*See* POLLUTION.)

Water is also an important agent of erosion. Rainfall helps to smooth rocks and move soil. Running water in rivers and streams cuts away the ground to form valleys. Water also carries sediment to the mouths of rivers to form deltas. Ocean waters are constantly eroding the coasts. Glaciers and ice sheets shape the landscape as they expand and retreat. (*See* EROSION.)

Water is used by people for transportation as well as recreation. Before the invention of the airplane, the only way to cross oceans was in ships. Most trade carried on with overseas countries is still done by shipping.

Behavior of water The chemical formula for water is H_2O. Water is a chemical compound consisting of two hydrogen (H) atoms and one oxygen (O) atom. About one part in every 4,500 in water is heavy water or deuterium. (*See* DEUTERIUM; HEAVY WATER.) Most water also contains a very small percentage of dissolved substances.

Water is the only substance known to humanity that occurs in three states within a convenient range of temperatures. The solid form of water is called ice and the gaseous form is called water vapor.

Water is liquid between 0°C [32°F] and 100°C [212°F]. At 0°C [32°F] or below, water freezes to become ice. Water expands when it freezes, and therefore is less dense than liquid water. (*See* DENSITY.) This is why ice floats on the tops of lakes and ponds during the winter. Huge blocks of ice called icebergs float in the polar oceans. Icebergs sometimes are a danger to shipping. Snow, sleet, and hail are frozen water that occurs as precipitation. (*See* ICE; PRECIPITATION; SNOW.)

At most temperatures on earth, water occurs as a liquid. Liquid water weighs about 1 kg per liter [62.4 lb per cu ft]. Liquid water has a very high surface tension. This means that drops of water tend to stick tightly together. For example, dripping water clings to a faucet before dropping. The chemical structure of water gives it its high surface tension. Separate water molecules are held together by hydrogen bonds. (*See* HYDROGEN BOND; SURFACE TENSION.) Most substances dissolve in water. This means that water is a good solvent. Water can dissolve rocks, minerals, dirt, and many other substances. Water is used for personal cleaning because it helps dissolve dirt and grime. (*See* SOLUTION AND SOLUBILITY.)

Water vapor is the gaseous form of water. When water reaches its boiling point of 100°C [212°F], it absorbs (takes in) heat before changing to steam. This absorbed heat is called latent heat. Steam contains much latent heat and it is thus used as a form of energy. The old Mississippi River steamboats were powered by steam.

Water vapor in the atmosphere has a tremendous effect on the weather. The latent heat of water vapor is released when water vapor condenses and falls as rain or snow. (*See* CONDENSATION.)

Atmospheric pressure (the weight of air pressing on the earth) affects the boiling point of water. At sea level, water boils at the usual 100°C [212°F]. At an altitude of 3,050 m [10,000 ft], where the atmosphere is much thinner, water boils at 90°C [194°F]. (*See* WATER VAPOR.)

People depend on water for life. They have developed complicated methods of purifying and transporting water. Much progress has been made in the desalination (removal of salt) of ocean water. Plant and animal life in water must be protected from the dumping of pollutants in their habitats. In this way, animals, plants, and human beings all will benefit from the earth's most valuable natural resource. *See also* OCEANOGRAPHY; WATER CYCLE. J.M.C./A.D.

WATERCRESS (wŏt′ ər kres′) Watercress (*Nasturtium officinale*) is a perennial (living many years) aquatic—water—plant that belongs to the mustard family. It grows on or under the surface of clear, cool streams and rivers in the Northern Hemisphere. Its stems and leaves that taste like pepper are a good source of vitamin C. They are often used in salads. *See also* MUSTARD FAMILY; NASTURTIUM. A.J.C./M.H.S.

WATER CYCLE (wŏt′ ər sī′ kəl) The water cycle is the journey of water from the oceans to the land and from the land back to the oceans. The water cycle is also called the hydrologic cycle. The main driving forces of the water cycle are the sun's heat, which causes the evaporation of water, and gravity.

The heat of the sun evaporates—takes up—water from the oceans. Air currents lift this evaporated water, or water vapor, into the atmosphere. As the air rises it cools. When the air reaches its dew point, it becomes saturated—it can hold no more water. (*See* DEW POINT.) The water then condenses into droplets or ice crystals, forming a cloud. Precipitation in the form of rain, sleet, or snow falls from these clouds.

In the water cycle shown in the picture below, water evaporates from large water bodies, such as oceans and lakes, to form clouds. When these clouds condense over land, water is returned to the oceans by rivers, or it seeps through the ground to be taken up eventually by plants.

Several things may happen to the precipitation if it falls on land. It may be absorbed, or taken in, by the soil. In this case, the water may be used by plants for nourishment or it may percolate—move—through the soil to form ground water. (*See* GROUND WATER.) Some of the precipitation may flow down slopes as runoff. This water may find its way to a river or stream. Eventually, the river or stream empties into a larger body of water. It is then evaporated again. Runoff is an important agent of erosion. (*See* EROSION.)

The water plants use is returned to the atmosphere by transpiration. (*See* TRANSPIRATION.) Animals return water through waste products, such as sweat.

In cold areas, most precipitation falls as snow. In polar regions or on high mountains, the snow may stay all year long. Eventually, the snow becomes ice. This mass of ice is called a glacier or ice sheet. About 2 percent of the earth's water is stored in glaciers and ice sheets. (*See* GLACIER AND ICE SHEET.)

The water cycle is necessary for all life on earth because it is constantly replenishing the earth's fresh water supply. *See also* PRECIPITATION; RAIN; WATER. J.M.C./R.W.L.

WATERFALL AND RAPID A waterfall (wŏt′ ər fôl′) is the falling of water from a higher level to a lower level. Waterfalls with a small volume, or amount, of water are called cascades. Cataracts are waterfalls with a large

Waterfalls are spectacular sights.

A simplified cross section of Niagara Falls shows how a hard layer of limestone caps layers of shale (green) and sandstone (red). Water is constantly undercutting the rocks beneath the limestone, and, from time to time, great slabs of limestone crash down. As a result, the falls are gradually retreating.

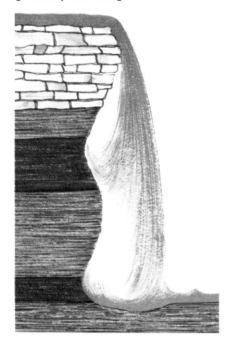

volume of water. A series of waterfalls is also sometimes called a cataract. Rapids (rap′ ədz) are cataracts that have small, sloping falls.

Waterfalls are characteristic of rivers that are young in geologic time. A river is constantly cutting away at the layers of rock beneath it. Sometimes, an area of soft rock occurs downstream from an area of hard rock. The soft rock erodes—is eaten away—much more quickly than the hard rock. After much erosion has occurred, a waterfall forms. Thus, the water flows downstream over the hard rock, then suddenly drops at the place of erosion, or waterfall. Often, soft rock lies underneath the hard rock at the ledge of the waterfall. This soft rock erodes because of the

swirling water at the base of the waterfall. This is called undercutting and it is found at Niagara Falls, where it is causing the cataract to recede—move back—by about 1 m [3.3 ft] a year. Almost all waterfalls are cut back in this way. Eventually, the river runs a smooth course, and the waterfall no longer exists.

Waterfalls are often found in mountainous areas. They are also found in areas that have been eroded by glaciers and ice sheets. *See also* EROSION. J.M.C./W.R.S.

WATER FLEA (wȯt′ ər flē) Water fleas are small, aquatic (living in water) crustaceans that belong to the genus *Daphnia*. They are not insects. A water flea is about 2 mm [0.08 in] long and is almost completely enclosed by a thin, transparent shell—one that can be seen through—called a carapace. It swims through the water with a jerky motion, using its antennae as oars. Five pairs of leglike appendages are constantly moving, creating a flow of water through the carapace. The water brings a supply of oxygen and food to the tiny animal. The water flea's beating heart can be seen through the shell. Water fleas are sold as food for tropical fish. *See also* CRUSTACEAN.

A.J.C./C.S.H.

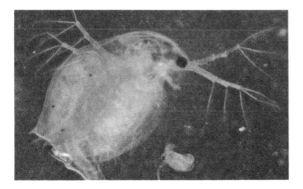

The gut of this water flea is filled with green algae. Young water fleas can also be seen, one below the mother and the rest inside the shell.

WATER GAS (wȯt' ər gas) Water gas is a mixture of the gases carbon monoxide and hydrogen. It is made by blasting steam through beds of very hot coke, a kind of coal. It is used in factories as a cheap fuel. However, it is not used so much now because of the use of natural gas. Pure water gas burns with a deep blue flame and is often called blue water gas. The heating value of blue water gas can be increased by spraying oil into it. The oil is then cracked to break up its molecules. (*See* CRACKING.) This produces light hydrocarbons, such as methane, that burn easily. The gas is then known as carbureted water gas.　　　　M.E./J.D.

WATER GLASS (wȯt' ər glas) Sand is made up mainly of a compound called silicon dioxide or silica. When sand is heated with sodium carbonate, a colorless, glassy solid is formed. This solid is made of a mixture of various sodium silicates. It can be dissolved in water to form a thick, colorless liquid called water glass. Water glass is used for cleaning. It may also be used to preserve eggs. To make a chemical garden, water glass is diluted with water. Colored crystals of various salts are then added to the solution. Crystals of cobalt nitrate (blue), manganese chloride (pink), and iron (II) sulfate (green) are some crystals that might be added. They react with the water glass to produce fantastic, colored growths that resemble plants. The growths are tubes of the metal silicates.

M.E./J.D.

WATER LILY (wȯt' ər lil' ē) The water lily is a beautiful aquatic (water) plant with large floating leaves. It is a dicotyledon belonging to the water lily family (Nymphaeaceae). The plants grow in both warm and hot climates. Water lilies grow long, stout stalks from the mud bottoms of clear, shallow lakes and ponds. The round leaves float on the surface, and the flowers grow just above them. The white-flowered water lily is the most common kind.

The Victoria regia—a water lily from the American tropics—is the largest water lily. Its leaves often measure more than 2 meters [6 ft] across. They have upturned edges and are strong enough to bear the weight of a small child.　　　　W.R.P./M.H.S.

The leaves of the large Victoria regia water lily are often more than 2 m [6 ft] wide.

WATER SOFTENING (wòt' ər sò' fən ing)
Water softening is the process by which calcium and magnesium are removed from
water. Water containing these substances is
called hard water. Hard water forms scales in
pipes and does not easily dissolve soaps or
detergents. Water softening is done in two
main ways: the lime-soda process and the
ion-exchange process.

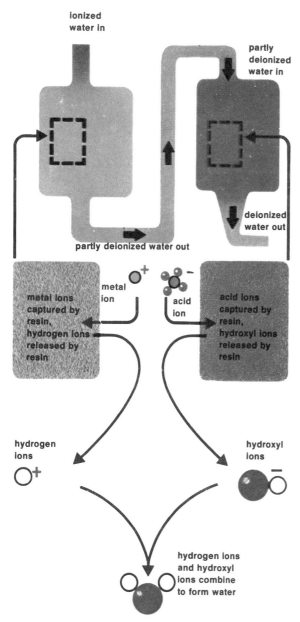

Deionization is a process that removes all salts from
water, including those that cause hardness. Thus
very pure, soft water is made.

The lime-soda process involves the addition of lime (calcium oxide) and soda ash to
hard water. There substances chemically
combine with the magnesium and calcium in
the hard water. The new chemical compounds, which do not dissolve in water, sink
to the bottom of the water tank. The lime-soda
process reduces the amount of magnesium
and calcium salts in the water to about 50 parts
per million.

The ion-exchange process reduces the
amount of calcium and magnesium salts to
about one part per million. This process involves passing water through a tank filled
with grains of zeolite. (*See* ZEOLITE.) As the
water passes through, the sodium ions of the
zeolite replace the magnesium and calcium
ions in the water. When most of the zeolite's
sodium has been replaced by calcium and
magnesium, a strong salt (sodium chloride)
solution is flushed through the system. This
salt solution removes the calcium and magnesium from the zeolite and replaces them
with sodium. Now the zeolite can continue to
soften the water.

These two water softening methods are
widely used in industry and homes in the
United States and Europe. *See also* WATER
SUPPLY.   J.M.C./A.D.

WATER SUPPLY (wòt' ər sə plī') A water
supply is the amount of readily available pure
water in a specific area. The water supply of
an area depends mainly on its rainfall. Most of
the United States, Europe, and other areas
with many people receive enough precipitation (rainfall and snowfall). Other areas, such
as the Mideast, most of Asia, and central
Australia receive little rain.

In the United States, most people get their
water from two sources: springs or wells and
public water systems. About 20 percent of
American households get their water from
springs and wells. This usually involves dig-
ging down to reach the ground water. The
ground water is then pumped up through a

well. Spring and well water may be impure and should be boiled before using it.

About 80 percent of American households receive their water from public water systems. The water is usually drawn from rivers, lakes, or reservoirs. Water from these sources must be purified—made fit to drink—by a complex series of treatments.

The first step in water treatment is pumping water from its source to a water treatment plant. The water then undergoes a treatment called coagulation. Harmless chemicals such as alum are added to the water. (*See* ALUM.) Suspended (undissolved) impurities in the water gather on the alum molecules to form flocs, or aggregates. The water is then passed through a settling tank where the flocs fall to the bottom and are removed.

Not all the impurities in the water form flocs. Therefore, a second treatment called sand filtration is needed. In sand filtration, the water is filtered through a big concrete tank that has a thick layer of fine sand on the bottom. Most of the impurities are removed in this step, although some bacteria that cause disease may remain.

To kill those bacteria, the water undergoes another treatment called chlorination. Chlorination involves the bubbling of chlorine gas through the water. The water is completely mixed so that it all gets chlorinated. Very low amounts of chlorine are enough to kill almost all of the bacteria that cause disease in the water. Although certain kinds of bacteria are left, they are not present in great enough numbers to cause the threat of disease. (*See* BACTERIA; CHLORINE.)

Water collects naturally in lakes, rivers, and large, open reservoirs, but it must be treated before we can drink it. Cities and towns have large water treatment plants. Untreated, or raw, water is pumped through filters that remove living and dead organic matter. Water is then oxidized to kill any remaining bacteria.

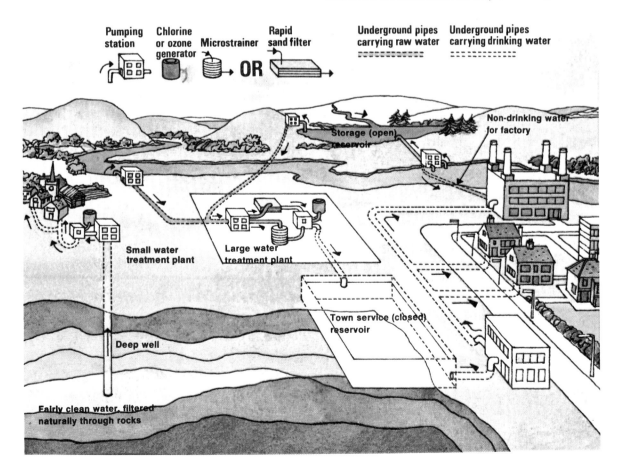

Pumping station — Chlorine or ozone generator — Microstrainer — Rapid sand filter — OR — Underground pipes carrying raw water — Underground pipes carrying drinking water

Non-drinking water for factory

Storage (open) reservoir

Small water treatment plant

Large water treatment plant

Deep well

Town service (closed) reservoir

Fairly clean water, filtered naturally through rocks

The final step of water purification involves testing the water to see how acidic or alkaline it is. The water is then neutralized by adding certain amounts of alkalis or acids to it. If the water is hard (contains amounts of dissolved calcium or magnesium), this also may be corrected at the plant. More often, however, hard water is treated at home. (*See* WATER SOFTENING.)

The water is now completely purified. From the water treatment plant, the water is pumped to underground reservoirs. The water is then pumped to homes, offices, and factories in the community.   J.M.C./R.W.L.

WATER TABLE (wòt' ər tā' bəl) The water table is the depth below which the ground is saturated with water (cannot hold more). When rain falls on land, some of it percolates (filters) through the soil until it reaches the zone of saturation. The top layer of the zone of saturation is called the water table. It is usually less than 30m [100 ft] beneath the surface. The water table arches beneath hills, roughly following the contour—bend—of the land above it. The water table rises and falls according to the amount of precipitation—rainfall and snowfall—above the surface. The lowest depth that the water table ever reaches is called the permanent water table. *See also* GROUND WATER.   J.M.C./W.R.S.

WATER VAPOR (wòt' ər vā' pər) Water vapor is the gaseous form of water. The sun's heat causes water to evaporate and change into water vapor. If water vapor cools to a temperature known as the dew point, it condenses into water droplets or ice crystals. These form clouds from which rain or snow may fall. (*See* CONDENSATION; EVAPORATION; PRECIPITATION.)

The content of water vapor in the atmosphere ranges from 4 percent over tropical rain forests to almost zero over deserts. The percentage of water vapor that the atmosphere can possibly hold at a certain temperature is called the relative humidity. *See also* HUMIDITY; WATER.   J.M.C./A.D.

WATSON,   JAMES   DEWEY (1928–   ) James Watson (wät' sən) is an American biochemist. He was born in Chicago, went into the university there at the age of 15, and graduated at age 19. He went to Cambridge, England, in 1951 and worked with Francis Crick. They were able to work out the way a molecule of DNA is arranged, from measurements done by Maurice Wilkins. This was a very important discovery, as it helped to explain how genes in chromosomes can make copies of themselves. This happens every time a cell divides to make two new cells. Each cell has a complete set of chromosomes, and they have to be perfect every time.

Watson shared the 1962 Nobel Prize for Medicine and Physiology with Crick and Wilkins for this discovery. *See also* CELL; CRICK, FRANCES HARRY; NUCLEIC ACID.

C.M./D.G.F.

WATT (wät) The watt is a unit of power. Power is the rate of doing work, or the work done per second. If the work done is equal to one joule and it takes one second, then the power is equal to one watt. (*See* JOULE.) A thousand watts is called a kilowatt. The power of electrical appliances is measured in watts or kilowatts. For example, an average light bulb is 100 watts. An electric fire is often 1 kilowatt. In electrical units, the power in watts is equal to the current in amperes multiplied by the voltage. In the foot-pound-second system of units, the unit of power is the horsepower. One horsepower is equal to 746 watts. The watt is named after the Scottish engineer James Watt.   M.E./A.I.

WATT, JAMES (1736–1819) James Watt (wät) was a Scottish engineer. He was born at Greenock, Renfrewshire, and was taught at home by his mother. When his mother died, his father had very little money. Watt traveled to London and served an apprenticeship as an instrument maker. Then he went back to Scotland and worked at the University of Glasgow.

At the university, Watt was asked to repair a model of Newcomen's steam engine. Watt became famous by improving this steam engine. In the Newcomen engine, the steam was condensed inside the cylinder. This meant that the cylinder was repeatedly being heated and cooled, causing heat to be wasted. Watt added a condenser for cooling the steam. The engine was then able to work more efficiently. In 1776, Watt perfected his new engine. Watt's steam engines were so much better than Newcomen's that he is often thought to have invented the first steam engine. He went on to build many more engines, making improvements all the time. One important device was the governor that regulates engine speed.

In 1781, he worked out a way to drive a wheel from the back-and-forth movement of a piston. This was the device that brought mechanization to many kinds of factories and workshops. Some fifty years later, George Stephenson used an engine of this kind to drive the first successful passenger train.

Watt also introduced a way of measuring the power of engines by comparing them with the power of a horse. He decided that a horse could raise a weight of 150 pounds by four feet in a second. He called this amount of power one horsepower. Horsepower is still used as a unit for measuring the power of engines. However, the scientific unit of power is now the watt (named for James Watt). One horsepower is equal to about 746 watts. *See also* STEAM ENGINE. C.M./D.G.F.

WAVE (wāv) A wave is a disturbance that occurs in a medium such as air, water, metal, or earth. In fact, waves commonly occur in nearly all physical matter—gases, liquids, solids, and vacuums.

A wave in water is one of the most familiar kinds of waves. Wind blowing across the ocean causes surface waves, which have crests and troughs. A crest is the top of a wave. A trough is the bottom. The strength of a wave is often measured by its amplitude, the distance between the top of the crest and the bottom of the trough. The stronger the wind blows, the higher the crests and the deeper the troughs will be on the water's surface. Beneath the surface, immense internal waves move through ocean waters.

There are many kinds of waves. A person beating a drum or blowing a trumpet causes vibrations in the air called sound waves. Light travels as electromagnetic waves. Transmissions to radios and television sets are in the form of electromagnetic waves, also. Earthquakes cause seismic waves; seaquakes cause tidal waves. A bullet shot from a high-powered rifle produces compressional waves; bomb blasts produce shock waves. A modern theory of matter proposes that all elementary atomic particles, such as electrons, protons, neutrons, and mesons, also have wavelike properties.

Waves have mechanical properties which can be observed and measured. When a wave moves along a medium, two things can be observed: the movement of the wave, and the movement of the medium. If a stone is thrown into the middle of a still pond, it will disturb the water (medium). Waves will move from the point of disturbance and travel toward shore, forming a pattern of enlarging rings. When the waves lose their energy and subside, the water will become still again.

Descriptions of waves take into account such properties as wavelength; the velocity, or speed, at which the wave travels; the density of the medium; and other physical factors related to space and time.

Huygens' Principle When a stone is dropped into still water, a ring of waves moves away from the point of disturbance. The ring grows larger and larger. Any short part of the wave front tends to form a straight waveline. If the straight wave passes through an opening in a barrier, the wave coming out the other side does not form a straight line, but spreads out in a curved line again. This changing of a straight wave front into a curved front is called diffraction.

Christiaan Huygens was a Dutch mathematician, physicist, and astronomer. In 1690, he proposed Huygens' Principle, which has been important to the understanding of wave behavior.

Huygens proposed that each point of an advancing wave front is in fact the center of a fresh disturbance, and the source of a new train of waves. For example, if two rooms are connected by an open doorway, and a person sounds a trumpet in a remote corner of one room, a person standing in any part of the other room will hear the trumpet sounds as if they were coming from the doorway. This is what actually happens. The vibrating air in the doorway is the source of sound waves that enlarge in all directions through the second room. The same principle is true of light that passes through a slit or breaks around the edge of an object. (*See* LIGHT; SOUND.)

Wavelength and frequency A wave is commonly referred to in terms of its wavelength or its frequency. Wavelength is the distance between two corresponding points on two consecutive waves. Wavelength is measured from crest to crest or from trough to trough, or from compression to compression.

Frequency, which is the rate of wave recurrence, is referred to in terms of cycles per

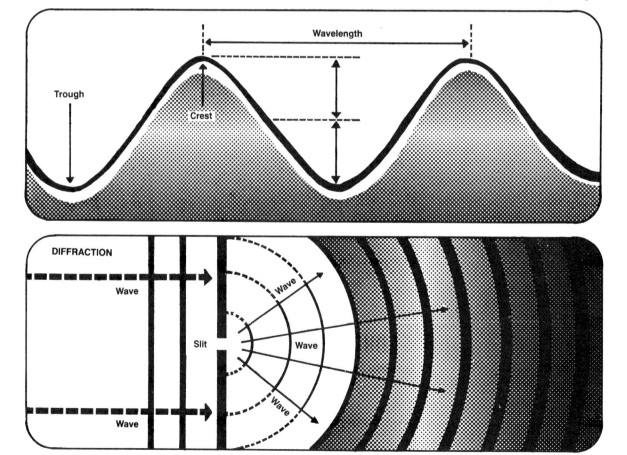

The top diagram shows the shape of a typical wave. The high point is called the crest; the low point is called the trough. The wavelength is the distance between two corresponding points on two consecutive waves. The bottom diagram shows diffraction. Waves traveling in a straight line diffract — spread out — when they pass through a slit.

second. Frequency is measured in units called hertz (Hz), after the German scientist Heinrich Hertz, who first produced and detected radio waves. High frequencies have short wavelengths; low frequencies have long wavelengths. (*See* FREQUENCY.)

Waves are said to be in phase when waves of the same frequency pass a given point at the same time. Waves of the same frequency make each other stronger when in phase, but cancel out each other when they are 180° out of phase. Physicists say that the two sources interfere with each other and refer to this wave phenomenon as interference. (*See* INTERFERENCE.)

In theory, light sometimes behaves as a particle and sometimes as a wave. In wave optics, electromagnetic radiation is capable of wave interference and other characteristics of waves. (*See* LIGHT.)

Wave motion applications The study of waves has many applications. Wave motion is applied to the construction of supersonic aircraft, wind tunnels, shock tubes, and rocket combustion. Radio and television stations transmit programs on precisely measured wave frequencies. Artificially generated seismic waves are employed in prospecting for gas and oil. The effects of nuclear bomb blasts, mining blasts, and sonic booms are measured in terms of compressional waves.

Ultrasonic and laser waves are used in special surgical procedures. X-ray waves are used to detect tumors and are used for the diagnosis and treatment of certain cancers. X rays can locate a kidney stone; a special biophysical instrument can shatter and disintegrate the kidney stone with sound waves.

Ocean wave motions are applied in the building of ships, submarines, and marine equipment. Navigation equipment and sonar systems are designed to recognize the influence of subsurface ocean waves.

Knowledge of sound waves and wave harmonics is applied to the building and tuning of pianos and organs and other string, brass, reed, and percussion instruments. Photographic equipment operates in response to controlled light wavelengths. Ultrasonic waves and X rays are used for industrial cleaning and inspection methods. Laser waves can be used to form three-dimensional images call holograms. *See also* ACOUSTICS; BIOPHYSICS; HOLOGRAPHY; MICROWAVE.

D.A.T./G.D.B.

WAX (waks) Wax is a solid, fatty substance that is widely used as a protective covering for many surfaces. It is also used to make candles and polishes. Wax is solid at room temperature but softens and becomes sticky when heated.

There are three kinds of wax: (1) mineral, (2) animal, and (3) vegetable. Mineral wax comes from petroleum (oil). It resists moisture and chemicals and has no odor. It is used on milk cartons, waxed paper, and polishes for automobiles, floors, and furniture. Animal wax, such as the beeswax produced by bees, is used to make candles and other products.

Many plants have a natural wax that protects them from heat and moisture. Carnuba, the hardest vegetable wax, is an important part of automobile wax and other polishes.

W.R.P./J.M.

WAXWING (wak' swing') A waxwing is a bird that belongs to the family Bombycillidae. It is a mostly brown bird, with white, black, and yellow feathers on its wings. The wings also have feathers with red, waxlike tips, for which the bird is named. A waxwing has a crest—pointed feathers on top of its head—similar to that of a cardinal. (*See* CARDINAL.) The bird grows 13 to 15 cm [5 to 6 in] in length.

There are two species of waxwings in North America. The Bohemian waxwing is found in the northwestern part of the continent. The cedar waxwing lives throughout most of the United States and Mexico and southern Canada. Both species eat berries and insects.   S.R.G./L.L.S.

Waxwings get their name from the fact that some of their wing feathers have waxy tips.

WEASEL (wē′ zəl) The weasel is a small, furry mammal that belongs to the weasel family Mustelidae. The most widespread species is the common weasel, which is found nearly everywhere in the Northern Hemisphere.

The common long-tailed weasel (*Mustea frenata*) is 30 to 46 cm [12 to 18 in] in length and weighs up to 340 g [12 oz]. It has a long, slender body covered with brown fur on the upper parts and white or yellow fur on the undersides. The fur of weasels that live in cold climates turns white in winter. This valuable fur is called ermine.

Weasels have a sharp sense of smell and are excellent hunters. They eat mice, squir-

The slender weasel feeds mainly on rodents.

rels, and other rodents. Weasels also raid farms and often kill more chickens than they can eat. The weasel's slim body enables it to squeeze through narrow openings when pursuing its prey. Weasels live in dens in rock piles and under tree stumps. They are mostly active at night, and their main enemy is the great horned owl.   W.R.P./J.J.M.

WEATHER

Weather (weth′ ər) is the day to day changes in the state of the earth's atmosphere. The study of the weather and the atmosphere is called meteorology. The typical weather for an area is called its climate. For example, the northeast region of the United States has a continental moist climate. This type of climate has four distinct seasons, a wide range in temperatures, and plenty of precipitation (rainfall and snowfall). (*See* ATMOSPHERE; CLIMATE.)

Causes of weather   The earth's atmosphere is constantly mixing air in an attempt to even out the temperature and pressure. The constant mixing results in weather. Water warms and cools more slowly than land. Thus, during the summer the oceans are cooler than the land. During the winter, however, the oceans are warmer than the land.

The tilt of the earth regulates the amount of sunlight a region gets. In high latitudes (toward the poles), the sun's rays are less effective than in low latitudes because they reach the earth at a greater angle. This means that bodies of cold air, or cold air masses, develop in the far north and far south, while warm air masses develop in the region near the equator. The warm air masses meet the cold air masses in the temperate zones, between the equator and the poles. The boundary region between the warm air and the cold air is called the polar front.

In the Northern Hemisphere, the polar front moves south during the winter and north during the summer. Movements of the polar front are mainly determined by strong winds high in the atmosphere. These winds are called the jet stream. The jet stream loops around the earth, forming ridges and troughs. Ridges cause high pressure (good weather) systems to form, while troughs cause low pressure (foul weather) systems to form. Low pressure systems that form along the polar front are called frontal, wave, or extratropical cyclones. A frontal cyclone gets much of its energy from the mixing of warm air south of the polar front with the cooler air north of the front. Frontal cyclones are most likely to strike the United States during the fall, winter, and early spring. The polar front moves into Canada around late spring. This is

why the summer weather is calmer and more predictable than the stormy, unpredictable winter weather. (*See* AIR MASS; CYCLONE; FRONT; JET STREAM.)

A tropical cyclone is a severe storm that develops over warm waters under certain conditions. It usually develops during the late summer and early fall. A mature tropical storm in the Atlantic Ocean is called a hurricane. Hurricanes sometimes strike the United States mainland as far north as New England. They may cause widespread damage, especially to coastal regions (*See* HURRICANE.)

The winds on earth flow in a general west to east direction, due to the rotation of the earth. This is why storms do not cross the Atlantic from Europe and hit the United States. (*See* EARTH; WIND.)

Below, a simple weather map shows some of the symbols used by meteorologists to show the weather across the country.

Elements of the weather Many different components make up the weather. Some con-

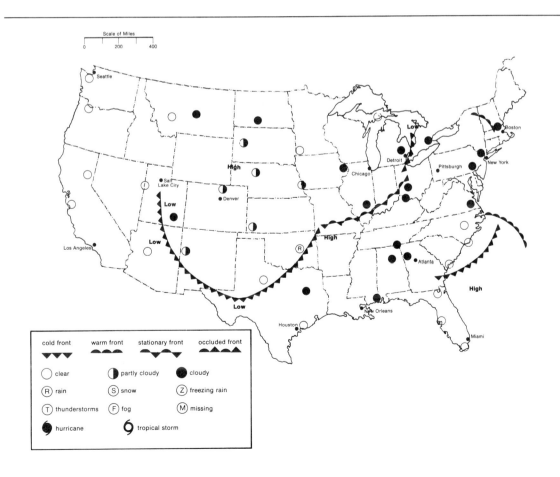

Weather stations contain all the instruments needed to measure weather features. The thermometer screen is used to take air temperatures in the shade. Other instruments measure sunlight, wind speed and direction, and amount of rain.

ditions of the atmosphere can be measured. These include temperature, air pressure, wind, and moisture.

The temperature is how warm or cold the air is. The temperature varies according to location. In the polar regions and high mountain ranges, the temperature is usually cold. In the tropics, the temperature is always warm at low altitudes. In the middle latitudes, the temperature changes between warm and cold. These differences are influenced by the angle of the sun's rays, the cloud cover, season, and the time of day. The temperature is measured

by an instrument called a thermometer. (*See* INSOLATION; THERMOMETER.)

Air pressure is important to weather forecasters. An air mass of high pressure usually means good weather. A low pressure air mass usually means bad weather. In the Northern Hemisphere, high pressure systems have a clockwise (anticyclonic) flow of air around the area of highest pressure. Low pressure systems have a counterclockwise (cyclonic) flow of air around the area of lowest pressure. Meteorologists measure the air pressure by an instrument called a barometer. If the barometer reading is dropping, weather forecasters predict poor weather. A rise in the pressure signals better weather. (*See* BAROMETER.)

The wind is the flow of air. In temperate

regions, wind is often caused by air flowing from a high pressure system into a low pressure system. Meteorologists can predict weather changes by tracking the wind flow. The speed and direction of the wind are measured by an instrument called an anemometer. (*See* ANEMOMETER; BEAUFORT SCALE.)

Moisture in the atmosphere forms clouds. The clouds produce all kinds of precipitation, including rain, snow, sleet, and hail. The moisture content of the air is called the humidity. Rainfall is measured in instruments called rain gauges. (*See* CLOUD; PRECIPITATION; RAIN GAUGE.)

Meteorologists make other readings, including visibility (the distance a person can see), cloud cover, cloud heights, and jet stream measurements. Many of the readings, such as cloud cover, are done by observation. Others, such as jet stream measurements, are done by radiosondes. Meteorological satellites, commonly called metsats, photograph the atmospheric state from outer space. (*See* RADIOSONDE; SATELLITE.)

Weather forecasting All the atmospheric conditions just described are put together to form a weather forecast. Computers around the country report the conditions every six hours from many weather stations. Meteorologists use the computer readouts to make weather maps. They draw lines of equal pressure, called isobars, and lines of equal temperature, called isotherms, to show the present weather patterns. (*See* ISOBAR AND ISOTHERM.) The complete weather map is called a synoptic chart, because it gives a general view, or synopsis, of the weather. Maps are also prepared of the upper atmospheric conditions. This is important for tracking the jet stream. Finally, a meteorologist can predict the weather with a degree of confidence.

Weather forecasts are most accurate for 24 to 48 hours. Long range forecasts are usually made of computer predictions on how the general weather will be for a week or month. Long range forecasts are not nearly as accurate as short range forecasts.

Many people blame meteorologists for bad weather. Meteorologists only predict what the weather is likely to be according to what has happened under similar conditions in the past. But they do not cause the weather that occurs; they are not responsible.

J.M.C./C.R.

WEATHERING (weth' ər ing) Weathering is the breaking and wearing down of rocks by the weather. Weathering plays an important part in the formation of soil and in the natural erosion (wearing down) of the land. There are two main kinds of weathering: mechanical weathering and chemical weathering.

Mechanical weathering acts upon rocks exposed to the air. These rocks are broken apart in several ways. Sometimes, rainwater enters a crack in a rock. If the temperature drops below 0°C (32°F), the water freezes into ice. When water freezes it expands. This expansion may break the rock. Weathered rocks occurring on a slope or mountainside may tumble down to form piles called talus or scree.

The surface of desert rocks are very hot during the day but cool off quickly at night. Extremes of temperatures cause the surface layer to expand and contract (move in and out). This may cause the rock's surface layer to break or peel off in layers by a process called exfoliation.

Plant roots break some rocks apart. The plant roots grow into narrow cracks. As the plant grows, the roots become thicker and break the rocks.

The main agent of chemical weathering is water. Water can dissolve many minerals. Streams, rivers, and rainfall all dissolve certain minerals in rocks. After the removal of these minerals, the rocks may crumble.

Rainwater may contain carbon dioxide

dissolved from the atmosphere. This forms a very weak acid (carbonic acid). When such rainwater comes in contact with limestone, it dissolves the limestone by a process called carbonation. Carbonation is responsible for karst scenery and the formation of limestone caves. *See also* EROSION; KARST SCENERY.

J.M.C./W.R.S.

times, they use the web only when not feeding. One type of webworm found in the eastern United States is the fall webworm. This webworm eats the leaves of fruit and forest trees. At times the web of the fall webworm is large enough to enclose a human being.

J.J.A./J.E.R.

European lackey moth caterpillars are sometimes called webworms. These larvae have just molted and the empty skins can be seen.

Weathering is especially noticeable on the steep slopes of exposed rock. Fragments of rock that have been shattered by mechanical weathering pile up to form scree.

WEBER (web' ər) The weber is an SI unit used in magnetism. (*See* INTERNATIONAL SYSTEM.) It measures the strength of a magnetic flux. The magnetic flux is the same as the number of lines of force made by a magnet or a magnetic circuit. The weber is defined as the flux linking a circuit of one turn that produces an electromotive force of 1 volt when reduced uniformly to zero in 1 second. The weber is named after the German physicist Wilhelm Weber (1804-1891). *See* MAGNETISM.

M.E./A.I.

WEBWORM (web' wərm') Webworm is the name for various types of moth caterpillars that spin a silky web or "tent" around part or all of their food plants. (*See* BUTTERFLY AND MOTH.) Webworms live in groups. At times, they feed only on the food plant under their web and make the web larger as they move on to new leaves. At other

WEED (wēd) A weed is any plant that grows where it is not wanted. In most cases, weeds are wild plants that grow quickly, often injuring or killing more wanted plants. Weeds are a main problem among almost every kind of cereal, fruit, and vegetable crop that is grown.

Some weeds are annual plants that complete their entire life cycles in only a few weeks. (*See* EPHEMERAL PLANT.) In a single growing season, these weeds may produce several generations and completely take over from other plants in the area. Some weeds are perennial plants (living many years) with extensive root systems. In some cases, these perennial weeds have widespread rhizomes. (*See* RHIZOME.) Weeds trouble farmers and gardeners throughout the world. They cause the destruction of billions of dollars worth of plants every year. Weeds can best be controlled by careful use of herbicides. *See also* HERBICIDE.

A.J.C./M.H.S.

WEEVIL (wē' vəl) Weevil is the name for a group of beetles (family Curculionidae) in which the head is drawn out into a snout. Jaws

Weevils are serious pests that are found in mosts parts of the world.

are at the end of the snout and the antennae are halfway up the snout. There are about 60,000 kinds of weevils, and this family is the largest in the animal kingdom. They are found on plants throughout the world. Many species are brightly colored. The colors are sometimes provided by a coating of scales or powder. This coating rubs off easily.

Many weevils lack hind wings and therefore cannot fly. Their front wings, or elytra, may not be movable. The grubs, or larvae, have no legs. Grubs often feed inside plant tissues. Roots, stems, flowers, leaves, and seeds are all attacked. The female weevil often uses her snout to drill a hole for her eggs.

Many species of weevils are serious pests. The boll weevil causes great losses in cotton fields. Grain weevils, which first fed on the seeds of wild grasses, have become troublesome pests where grain is stored. Weevil larvae usually do most of the damage, but the adults are not all blameless. Pine weevils, for example, feed on the bark of young conifer shoots and cause distortion of the branches. *See also* BEETLE.   J.J.A./J.E.R.

WEIGHT (wāt′) Weight is the force put forth by gravity on an object. It is very easy to confuse weight with mass. Really they are not the same thing. The mass of an object is the amount of material that it contains. The weight is the force with which that amount of material is pulled to the ground by gravity. On the earth we often use the same units of measurement, such as kilograms, pounds, and tons, for both weight and mass. This is the cause of the confusion. Scientists, using the International System of Units (SI), measure mass in kilograms and measure weight in the unit of force called the newton.

The pull of gravity varies slightly in different parts of the world. An object with a mass of one kilogram may weigh one kilogram at sea level, and less than a kilogram at the top of Mount Everest. And if it were taken to the moon, its weight would be only one-sixth of a kilogram. The moon's gravity is one-sixth of the earth's. The mass of the object would not change. It would still be one kilogram.

A spring balance measures the weight of an object, because it is stretched by the pull of gravity on the object. A pair of scales, however, measures actual mass, because the object is balanced against a mass in the other pan. A pair of scales is not affected by a change in gravity.   D.M.H.W./J.D.

WEIGHTLESSNESS (wāt′ ləs nəs)
Weightlessness occurs when there is no pull of gravity on a body. It can happen in a spacecraft when it is far away from the earth or other planets. It can also happen when a satellite orbits the earth. If the force of gravity is balanced by the centrifugal force, the satellite is in a state of weightlessness.

Weightlessness causes problems in spacecrafts. Anything that is not fixed or tied down floats in midair. Astronauts use special devices to be able to eat and drink. Crew members have to learn to adjust the vigor of their actions to keep from crashing into the walls and equipment. Sometimes, weightlessness causes nausea and giddiness, because the working of the balancing organs in the inner ear is upset. Astronauts are able to adapt to weightlessness in a short time through training.

Because on earth our muscles are normally being used to work against gravity, they get a certain amount of exercise all the time. To make up for the lack of gravity, regular exercise is essential in a spacecraft to keep the muscles in good condition. While in space, astronauts tend to "grow" taller. This is because the pads of cartilage between the bones of the spine are no longer under pressure from gravity, and they expand. The increase in height, which may be as much as 5 cm [2 in], disappears when the astronauts return to earth.

Under weightless conditions, it is possible to conduct certain scientific experiments that are impossible on earth. Absolutely perfect crystals can be grown, for example, and alloys of different metals can be formed which are very difficult to make under the pull of gravity.   D.M.H.W./J.D.

WELDING AND CUTTING Welding (weld′ ing) is a means of joining similar metals by melting them, bringing them together so that they fuse (blend together), and then allowing the fused metal parts to harden.

Welding involves very high temperatures. The temperatures are often produced by jets of burning gases. Oxygen and acetylene are often used, producing an oxyacetylene flame. Another flame that can be used is the oxyhydrogen flame.

The flame heats the metal parts to be joined until the surfaces become molten metal and fuse together. Additional metal may be added to the joint by melting wires or rods. The extra metal is added and built up around the parts to make a solid joint.

There are many different kinds of welding. Electric arc welding uses a heavy current of electricity passed between electrodes. This kind of welding is often used in automatic welding machines. In atomic hydrogen welding, a stream of hydrogen gas is passed between two tungsten electrodes and an electric arc is struck between the electrodes. Atomic hydrogen welding is used for high-quality alloy steels. Other kinds of welding use beams of electrons, intense beams of laser light, and streams of gas so hot that they become plasmas. (*See* PLASMA.)

Welding is an extremely important process in engineering. It may be used to join metal pipes, to fix the parts of bridges tightly together, and to construct the metal frames of buildings. It is also used in shipbuilding and in the aircraft industry. Using rivets or nuts and bolts to join parts in a structure adds weight to the structure. This is one instance in which welding is better than the other ways of joining parts, because it does not add as much weight. Large metal structures can now be made by joining smaller pieces together on the spot. In the past it was necessary to cast large amounts of metal in molds.

Cutting (kət′ ing) through metals by means of concentrated, very hot flames is widely used in heavy industry. Sheets of steel or other metal can be shaped with such cutting

A modern welding technique uses a high-powered beam of electrons.

Above, a busy welding shop, in which parts of automobile bodies are being spot welded, a common way of joining large metal structures.

flames. Thermal cutting is often used in the shipbuilding industry and in structural engineering. A cutting torch is used. This heats the steel to a point at which it is ready to ignite. A jet of oxygen is then passed through the center of the flame, and the iron in the steel actually burns into iron oxide. The burnt metal sprays from the other side of the cut in showers of sparks.

This method can only be used on steel that does not contain much chromium. Steel that contains a high proportion of chromium forms oxides, which burn at a much higher temperature. To counteract this, powdered iron may be blown in with the jet of oxygen. This lowers the melting point of the waste metal or slag. Thermal cutting can be performed automatically or by hand. *See also* SOLDERING AND BRAZING. D.M.H.W./A.I.

WERTHEIMER, Max (1880–1943) Max Wertheimer (vərt′ hī′ mər) was a German psychologist. He is best known for founding a school of psychological thought based on the concept of ''gestalt.''

The idea of Gestalt psychology is that every experience is a complete happening. The word is German, and cannot be exactly translated, but it means something like ''pattern.'' The opposite of gestalt is the idea that things are composed of lots of little bits. Gestalt means that the little bits add up to more than just their total when they are part of an emotion or experience. For example, a picture of a cat is not just a collection of lines but an image of a cat. The ''cat'' means more than the collection of lines would. It may also have different associations for different people. The gestalt theory is based on the way we see things. According to Wertheimer, since we see things as whole pictures, that is how our minds work. *See also* PERCEPTION; PSYCHOLOGY. C.M./D.G.F.

WHALE (wāəl) Whales are aquatic mammals belonging to the order Cetacea. A few species live in fresh water, but most species live in the sea. They have a streamlined shape and a powerful tail to drive them forward. With its two large horizontal fins or flukes, the tail produces the driving force by beating strongly up and down. Flippers at the front are used for steering and balance. The hind limbs of whales have completely disappeared, apart from a few small bones inside the body. Body hair has also disappeared, giving whales a smoother outline and less resistance to water. Instead of hair, whales are insulated by a thick layer of fat, or blubber, under the skin. The blubber may be as much as 61 cm [2 ft] thick on some parts of the body. Besides protecting the animal against the cold, the blubber is an important food reserve.

Most of the best-known whales are large creatures. For example, the blue whale reaches a length of more than 30 m [100 ft]. However, many whales, such as dophins and porpoises, are small. Some are only 1.5 to 1.8 m [5 to 6 ft] long.

Whales live entirely in water. Sometimes, whales are stranded on the shore. Although they are air-breathing animals, they soon die because their great weight keeps them from expanding (opening out) the chest cavity. They can breathe easily when afloat, because the water supports most of their weight.

The bottle-nosed whale has been known to stay under water for about two hours. The sperm whale can dive down to depths of 500 fathoms. (*See* FATHOM.) Such long and deep dives are unusual. Most dives last between 10 and 30 minutes. Whales have special mechanisms that help them to stay under water. When they breathe, they renew about nine-tenths of the air in their lungs. When human beings breathe in, only about one-fourth of the air is renewed. Whales therefore have a fairly large supply of fresh air to start with. They also have an additional oxygen supply in the muscles, where air is loosely held in combination with a pigment called myohaemoglobin. Another thing that helps whales hold their breath for long periods of time is their low sensitivity to carbon dioxide in the blood.

(It is the carbon dioxide building up in human blood that affects the brain and makes the human being take another breath.) (*See* RESPIRATION.)

When a whale surfaces to renew its air supply, it needs only to push the top of its snout out of the water. This is because the nostril or blowhole is at the top of the head. The expelled air is forced out strongly to form the spout or blow.

Living whales are divided into two groups—tooth whales and whalebone whales. Tooth whales, which include most species, generally have many conical teeth and eat mainly squids and fishes. The killer whale feeds on seals. One African river dolphin feeds mostly on plants. Other tooth whales include the narwhal and the sperm whale.

Whalebone whales have no teeth. Their mouths contain huge comblike fringes of baleen or whalebone. This horny substance is usually black. All whalebone whales feed by straining small animals from the water. The mouth is filled with water and the water is then forced out through the fringes by the tongue. The animals caught in the baleen are swept into the stomach by the tongue. All whalebone whales are large animals, which are usually found in cold seas. They include the blue whale, the right whales, and the rorquals.

The future of many of the larger kinds of whales is uncertain. Whalers have killed so many blue, bowhead, humpback, and right whales that those species are threatened with extinction. Overhunting has also greatly reduced the number of fin and sei whales. Also, if the human population does not stop increasing, people may have to compete with whales for food in the sea. Some nations have begun fishing for krill. Krill is the chief food of whales in Antarctic waters. *See also* DOLPHIN; KRILL; NARWHAL; PORPOISE; RIGHT WHALE; RORQUAL; SPERM WHALE.

J.J.A./J.J.M.

WHEAT (wēt′) Wheat is the second most important food crop in the world. Only rice feeds more people than this familiar grain. However, wheat crops cover more of the earth's surface than rice or any other crop. Farmers of the world grow over 453 million metric tons [498.3 million short tons] of wheat a year. Hundreds of millions of people throughout the world use wheat as their main source of food.

This great field of wheat (above) is being harvested by one person and a machine. Before such machines existed, farm workers mowed wheat with scythes and gathered it into bundles called sheaves, which were stacked into shocks. The grain was separated from the stalks by threshing and winnowing. Today, machines carry out all these processes in a fraction of the time.

The wheat plant belongs to the grass family, Gramineae. It is bright green in color until harvest time when it turns golden brown. Wheat plants grow 1.3 m [4.3 ft] high. The leaves are long and slender, and the wheat head that holds the kernels is at the top of the main center stem. The average plant produces 50 kernels of wheat. The kernels are about 3 to 6 mm [.12 to .25 in] long and divided into three parts. These are the germ, the bran, and the endosperm. The germ is where the growth starts after the seed is planted. Wheat germ is used in some breakfast cereals and is also eaten as a food alone. The bran is made up of several layers. It protects the germ much like a shell protects a nut. The bran is used primarily in livestock feed. The endosperm is the most important part of the wheat kernel. It makes up about 85 percent of the kernel. The endosperm is used in making bread and other baked goods. It contains gluten, a substance that makes dough rise in the presence of yeast. The last part of the kernel, the husk, is called the chaff.

Wheat is harvested by giant, self-propelled machines called combines, which cut, thresh (separate the germ, bran, and endosperm from the chaff), and clean the wheat. The kernels are then stored in tall cylindrical buildings called grain elevators. Later, the kernels are transported to factories where they are milled (ground) into flour for use in baking. About 543 million bushels of wheat are ground into 10.9 billion kg [24 billion lb] of flour each year in the United States. The average American uses about 49 kg [107 lb] of wheat a year.

Wheat is also made into breakfast cereals, macaroni products, and livestock and poultry feeds. The Soviet Union is the largest producer of wheat in the world with a yearly crop of over 3 billion bushels. The United States is the second-leading grower of wheat. The country's top wheat-producing states have a yearly yield of over 300 million bushels. North Dakota, Kansas, Oklahoma, and Montana are states that have large wheat crops.

W.R.P./F.W.S.

WHIPPOORWILL (hwip′ ər wil′) The whippoorwill (*Caprimulgus vociferus*) is a bird found in North America and Central America. The bird is named for its whistled call, which sounds like "whip-or-will, whip-or-will."

The whippoorwill's body is about 25 cm [10 in] long. The bird has brown, spotted feathers that blend in with wooded surroundings. Whippoorwills are normally active at night. Because of their soft feathers, whippoorwills fly silently. Like swallows, they fly with their bills wide-open to catch insects.

The female usually lays two white, lilac-and-brown marked eggs on the ground. Whippoorwills, like many birds, are a natural help to farmers. The birds eat some insects that often damage crops.   J.J.A./L.L.S.

WHIRLIGIG (hwer′ li gig′) The whirligigs are a group of 700 species of water beetles that belong to family Gyrinidae. They swim in circles along the surface of quiet ponds and lakes. Their smooth, oval, boat-shaped bodies are a shiny bluish-black or olive green color. The front legs are long and adapted for holding prey. The middle and rear legs are

The compound eyes of the whirligig (left) allow it to see both above and below water. Whirligigs have well-developed wings and are excellent fliers.

broad, paddle-shaped, and fringed with hairs. The whirligig uses these broad legs to move itself forward across the water's surface. If threatened, a whirligig may release a foul-smelling, milky liquid.

The compound eyes of the whirligig are divided into upper and lower halves. The upper halves watch the activity above the water surface while the lower halves look underwater. Whirligigs have well-developed wings and are excellent fliers.

A female whirligig deposits her eggs on underwater plants. The eggs hatch into larvae that breathe through gills and prey on aquatic insects. *See also* BEETLE.   J.M.C./J.E.R.

WHITEFISH (hwīt' fish') A whitefish is a freshwater fish that belongs to the family Salmonidae. It is closely related to the salmon and trout. (*See* SALMON; TROUT.) It is a plain, silvery fish that lives in cold, northern lakes and rivers. A whitefish feeds on plankton and is eaten by many other fish and animals, including humans. (*See* PLANKTON.) The whitefish was an important commercial fish in the Great Lakes until overfishing and environmental changes caused the decline of the fish. (*See* ENVIRONMENT.) There are 21 species of whitefish in North America. Many are nearly extinct.   S.R.G./E.C.M.

WHITNEY, ELI (1765–1825) Eli Whitney (hwit' nē) was an American inventor. He was born at Westboro, Massachusetts. He was working as a teacher in Savannah, Georgia, when he visited a cotton plantation. During his visit he saw there was a need for a machine to separate the seeds from the cotton fibers. He built his first cotton gin in 1793. It could pick out the seeds from the cotton as fast as 50 people could. The cotton gin helped the cotton industry grow.

When Whitney made a contract with the American government in 1798 to make muskets, he developed an even greater invention. Until then, guns were all made by hand. Each gun was made of parts that fit only that gun. Whitney designed machine tools that allowed even unskilled workers to make perfect parts. Guns could be assembled from these parts without any more machine work being done on them. Also, guns with broken parts could be repaired with spare parts. This was mass production.   C.M./D.G.F.

WHITTLE, SIR FRANK (1907–   ) Frank Whittle (hwit' əl) is the British engineer who invented the jet engine. He was born in Coventry and joined the Royal Air Force (RAF) as an apprentice. He first became a fighter pilot. Later he was sent by the RAF to study engineering at Cambridge University. As an engineer he worked on the development of gas turbines for the jet propulsion of aircraft. In May 1941, Whittle's first jet-powered aircraft was tested. By the end of World War II, in 1945, many squadrons of jet airplanes were being flown. Since then jet engines have been developed so that all large commercial and military planes are powered by them. All these engines are based on Whittle's design.   C.M./D.G.F.

WIENER, NORBERT (1894–1964) Norbert Wiener (wē' ner) was an American mathematician and the founder of the science of cybernetics. He was born in Columbia, Missouri. Wiener was a highly talented child. He could read and write when he was three years old. He received a Ph.D. degree from Harvard University when he was 18.

Wiener joined the Massachusetts Institute of Technology in 1919. He retired as professor in 1960. While he was there he pioneered the science of cybernetics. This is the theory of how computers work. Wiener was especially interested in the similarity between computers and the human brain. He wrote books on the subject of cybernetics and contributed greatly to the theory and technology of automation. *See also* AUTOMATION; CYBERNETICS.   C.M./D.G.F.

WILLOW FAMILY The willow (wil′ ō) family contains two genera: *Populus*, the poplars with 30 species; and *Salix*, the willows with 320 species. They are trees and shrubs with simple, alternate leaves. Clusters of staminate (male) or pistillate (female) flowers form catkins on separate plants. (*See* DIOECIOUS.) In the genus *Populus*, the catkins droop from the branches. In the genus *Salix*, the catkins are upright. Most members of the willow family grow in nothern temperate areas.

The black willow (*Salix nigra*) is a valuable lumber tree that grows in the eastern United States. Weeping willow (*Salix babylonica*) and pussy willow (*Salix discolor*) are two popular members of the willow family. *See also* CATKIN; POPLAR.

A.J.C./M.H.S.

WILTING (wilt′ ing) Wilting is the drooping and drying out of the leaves and stem of a plant. Wilting may be caused by lack of water. Quite often, however, wilting is the symptom of a plant disease. These diseases may be caused by bacteria, fungi, or viruses.

A fungus called *Fusarium* causes potato, cotton, and other plants to wilt. Many elm trees have died because of a fungal disease called Dutch Elm disease. Various other plant diseases kill thousands of plants each year.

A dehydrated plant may recover from wilting by watering. Most disease-caused wilting is fatal to the plant. Preventive measures against wilting should be taken while the plant is still young. *See also* PLANT DISEASE.

J.M.C./M.H.S.

WIND

Wind (wind′) is the movement of air. Wind has an important effect on the weather. Winds blow both at the surface and at the higher levels of the atmosphere.

The direction of the wind is the direction from which it comes. For example, a north wind blows from north to south, while a southeast wind blows from southeast to northwest.

Prevailing winds The prevailing winds are the chief wind belts on earth. They are caused by the uneven heating of the atmosphere and the rotation of the earth. The uneven heating causes the warmer air to rise. The rotation of the earth causes winds in the northern hemisphere to be deflected (bent) to the right. The reverse happens in the southern hemisphere. (*See* CORIOLIS FORCE.) The prevailing winds from both the northern and the southern hemispheres together are called the general circulation.

The area within 30° north and south of the equator is where the trade winds are generated. Air at the surface is heated by the sun. The hot air rises as high as 18,000 m [60,000 ft]. The rising air is replaced by surface air. This rising and replacing of air produces a belt of winds on either side of the equator called the trade winds. The trade winds blow in a general east to west direction.

Near the equator, there is an area of calm winds called the doldrums. The doldrums occur because the air at the equator is rising instead of blowing along the surface. At about 30° north and south of the equator, the rising air from the doldrums moves downward back to the surface. The downward-moving air produces no winds. This region is called the horse latitudes.

Between 30° and 60° north and south of the equator, winds blow in a general west to east direction. These winds are called the prevailing westerlies. The prevailing westerlies are caused by the movement of surface air from the equator toward the poles. The prevailing westerlies play an important role in the weather of the United States.

The polar easterlies are winds that occur between the poles and 60° north and south of

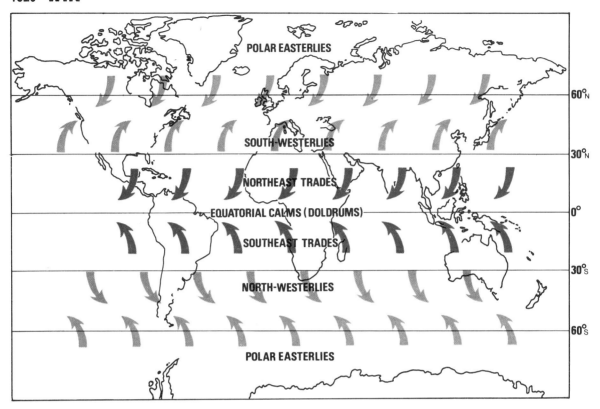

POLAR EASTERLIES

60°N

SOUTH-WESTERLIES

30°N

NORTHEAST TRADES

EQUATORIAL CALMS (DOLDRUMS)

0°

SOUTHEAST TRADES

30°S

NORTH-WESTERLIES

60°S

POLAR EASTERLIES

The map (above) shows the prevailing wind belts on earth. These winds are caused by the uneven heating of the atmosphere and the rotation of the earth. Prevailing winds were very important to seamen on sailing ships.

the equator. The polar easterlies are caused by the movement of heavy, cold air from the polar regions toward the equator. The polar easterlies blow in a general east to west direction.

Secondary circulation Winds that occur within the general circulation are part of the secondary circulation. These winds are usually associated with areas of high and low atmospheric pressure. Air flows into low pressure areas and out of high-pressure areas. In the northern hemisphere, air circulates around a high-pressure system in a clockwise (anticyclonic) direction. Winds circulate around a low-pressure system in a counterclockwise (cyclonic) direction. In the southern hemisphere, these directions are reversed. (*See* CYCLONE; DEPRESSION.)

Local winds Local winds occur in certain parts of the world. They are often affected by some geographic feature like a mountain or ocean. Monsoons are local winds caused by the heating of land during the summer, which is followed by cooling during the winter. The cooler, heavier ocean air blows onto land during the summer. During the winter, the cooler air over the land blows offshore. Monsoons have a great affect on the climate of southern Asia. (*See* MONSOON.)

Other local winds include chinooks, foehns, siroccos, and northers. Dry winds that blow down the sides of mountains are called chinooks in the western United States and foehns in the Alps. A sirocco is a local wind which carries hot air from the Sahara to the Mediterranean region of Europe. A norther is a bitter, cold, north wind that come before the arrival of a polar high-pressur

A model (facing right) of a supersonic plane is being tested in a wind tunnel. The smooth airstreams show how well this plane is streamlined.

area. During the winter, northers often cause a great decrease, or drop, in the temperature of the air.

Measurement of wind The speed and direction of wind is measured by an instrument called an anemometer. The wind direction can also be determined by a weather vane. Jet-stream winds are measured by instrument-laden weather balloons called radiosondes. The Beaufort scale is a table which has numbers to measure wind speed. The numbers range from 1 to 17. For example, a Beaufort scale wind of 4 is named a moderate breeze. A moderate breeze blows at 20 to 28 km [13 to 18 mi] per hour. A Beaufort scale wind of 11 is named a storm. A storm wind blows at 103 to 117 km [64 to 73 mi] per hour. Meteorologists have also found ways of measuring the windchill factor. The windchill factor is an indication of how much colder the wind makes the air feel. *See also* ANEMOMETER; BEAUFORT SCALE.

J.M.C./C.R.

WIND TUNNEL (wind′ tən′ əl) A wind tunnel is a tube with instruments for testing the effects of wind on airplanes, cars, and other objects. By using an electric blower or turbine, a strong wind can be generated in the wind tunnel. The wind speed may be over the speed of sound. Usually a scale model of the object to be tested is suspended from a balance device. The balance records the forces acting on the model as the air rushes past it. Other physical conditions, such as temperature and pressure, are also regulated.

Sometimes, smoke is placed in the tunnel to make the airflow visible. Wind tunnels are a necessary testing device for airplane and automobile designs. *See also* AERODYNAMICS; AIRPLANE.

J.M.C./R.W.L.

WIRE (wīr′) Wire is usually made from rods of metal by the process known as drawing. The metal rod is pulled through a tapered (narrow at one end) hole in a hard metal block called a die. To make the wire smaller, it is passed through different dies until the needed size is reached.

When steel wire is being produced, it is first heated until it is red-hot and then it is cooled slowly. This is called annealing, which keeps the wire from becoming brittle as it is drawn through the dies. After each drawing stage, the wire is wound on a drum. Then the wire passes to the next die. As the wire becomes thinner, it becomes longer. The next drum has therefore a larger diameter and turns more quickly to take up the extra length of wire.

Drawing the wire in this way increases the strength of the metal. A cable made up of several strands of wire is actually stronger than a rod of metal of the same size as the cable. Wire can be used in long lengths, or it can be chopped up into short lengths to make nails, pins, staples, or clips. D.M.H.W./A.I.

Copper wire (above), awaiting dispatch at a factory, is shown. Copper wire may be used as an electrical conductor.

WISTERIA (wis tir′ ē ə) Wisteria, also genus *Wisteria,* is the name for a group of climbing plants belonging to the pea family. The type of wisteria seen around various buildings in the United States is often the Chinese wisteria (*Wisteria sinensis*). A very showy plant, it has clusters of bluish violet blossoms. The flower clusters of the wisteria are from 30 to 61 cm [1 to 2 ft] long. One wisteria plant is reported to have covered almost 93 sq m [1,000 sq ft] of wall space. Wisteria pods and seeds contain a poison. If a person eats the pods or seeds, he or she may develop an awful stomach pain.

J.J.A./M.H.S.

Wisteria on a garden trellis is pictured above. Wisteria is a climbing plant which belongs to the pea family. Its pods and seeds contain a poison.

WITCH HAZEL FAMILY The witch hazel (wich′ hā′ zəl) family includes 28 genera and 140 species of trees and shrubs that live in tropical and temperate areas throughout the world. They have alternate, simple leaves and clusters of small flowers. The fruits are dry and woody.

American witch hazel (*Hamamelis virginiana*) grows in the eastern United States and Canada. Its forked twigs were once used as divining rods that were supposed to be able to locate underground water. This and other superstitions led to the plant's name. The bark and leaves can be distilled in alcohol to produce witch hazel lotion. This lotion is used to treat bruises, ulcers, skin problems, and inflammation. *See also* DISTILLATION.

A.J.C./M.H.S.

A sprig of witch hazel is shown above.

WOLF (wu̇lf′) The wolf is a wild, carnivorous mammal closely related to the domestic dog. (*See* DOG.) Wolves may be found in the wilderness areas of North America, Greenland, Europe, and Asia. The animals have a fairly broad head, powerful jaws, and short ears. The ears always stand erect. Male wolves generally weigh more than 45 kg [100 lb], and females often weigh less.

The two main species of wolf are the timber wolf, more often called the gray wolf (*Canis lupus*), and the red wolf (*Canis rufus*). Gray wolves are so called because of their thick, gray fur. The arctic wolf, which is of the same species as the gray wolf, may be pure white. The red wolf gets its name from its reddish fur.

Wolves usually have strong family units. Wolf families, often called wolf packs, remain together for long periods. A wolf uses its howl to tell other wolves of its presence. The howling sound helps keep the pack together.

Female wolves have a gestation period of about two months. (*See* GESTATION PERIOD.) A litter usually consists of four to six babies called "pups."

Wolves are in danger of extinction. Farmers and ranchers have killed many wolves because the animals sometimes attack livestock. Many people are afraid of wolves, though the animals would rather stay away from human beings.   J.J.A./J.J.M.

WOLFFIA (wŭl' fē ə) *Wolffia*, or watermeal, is a genus of tiny, floating aquatic plants found in ponds and streams. They are the smallest flowering plants known to humans. The entire plant is less than 0.13 cm [0.05 in] across. The *Wolffia* is a monocotyledon. *See also* DUCKWEED.

W.R.P./M.H.S.

WOLFRAM *See* TUNGSTEN.

WOLVERINE (wŭl' və rēn') The wolverine (*Gulo gulo*), probably the largest member of the weasel family, is related to badgers, skunks, and otters. Actually, the wolverine looks like a small bear with a long tail. The animal is sometimes called "the glutton" because it has an enormous appetite. It eats various small mammals and birds but feeds largely on animals, such as deer, that have been killed by other carnivores. The wolverine frequently kills more animals than it can eat. The wolverine often buries uneaten

The wolverine is probably the largest member of the weasel family. The body of an average-size weasel is about 76 cm [2.5 ft] long.

food or carries it up into a tree for safekeeping.

Wolverines have a body length of about 76 cm [2.5 ft]. The animal's coat consists of dark, shaggy hair with tan markings.

Wolverines once roamed the northern woods of Europe, Asia, and North America. The animals are rare today because they have been hunted extensively for their fur.

J.J.A./J.J.M.

WOMBAT (wäm′ bat′) The wombat, sometimes called the Australian badger, is a thickly built marsupial related to the koala. (*See* KOALA; MARSUPIAL.) Wombats are found in southern Australia and on the island of Tasmania. The animal's fur is often grayish brown or a yellow black. The wombat is about 91 cm [3 ft] long.

The wombat's strong, short legs are used to dig out the long burrows in which it lives.

Wombats are nocturnal (active at night). They leave their burrows to feed on grass and other plants.

The fur of the wombat is used to make long-wearing rugs. Some people keep wombats as pets.

J.J.A./R.J.B.

The wombat (above) is related to the koala bear.

WOOD (wüd′) Wood is the tough, nonliving part of a tree beneath the bark. It is

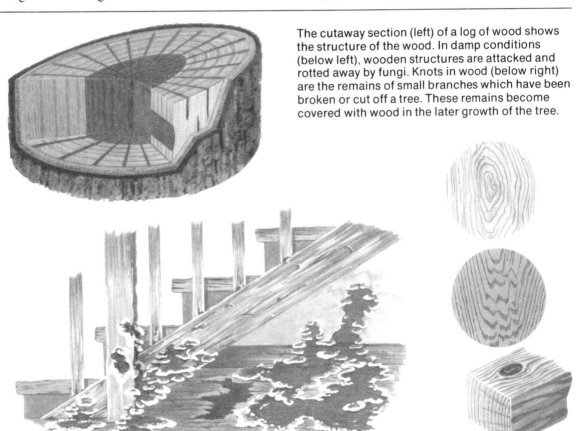

The cutaway section (left) of a log of wood shows the structure of the wood. In damp conditions (below left), wooden structures are attacked and rotted away by fungi. Knots in wood (below right) are the remains of small branches which have been broken or cut off a tree. These remains become covered with wood in the later growth of the tree.

mostly cellulose fiber and makes up the greatest part of a fully-grown tree. There are two layers of wood: sapwood and heartwood. The sapwood is located just under the bark. It contains xylem vessels that carry water. (*See* XYLEM.) The heartwood is the portion that runs from the sapwood to the center of the trunk or branch. It is made up of older xylem. Heartwood is heavier and darker than sapwood because it contains gums, resins, and tannin, a reddish coloring agent.

The pattern found in wood is called the figure. It contains marks such as growth rings, knurls, and knots. Growth rings are thin, wavy, dark-colored lines in the wood that show the tree's annual growth. (*See* ANNUAL RING.) Knurls and knots are small dark-colored circular marks that are places where branches once were located. Some woods also contain light and dark streaks in the heartwood known as pigment figures.

There are hardwoods, such as oak, and softwoods, such as pine. Spruce and fir are examples of medium-hard woods. Almost 50 percent of all wood cut in the United States is made into lumber. (*See* LUMBER.) Another 34 percent is ground into wood pulp to make paper. The remainder is used to make fine furniture, veneers, plywoods, poles, posts, pilings, and home heating fuel. *See also* HEARTWOOD; TREE.   W.R.P./M.H.S.

WOODCHUCK *See* GROUNDHOG.

WOOD LOUSE (wȕd′ laȕs′) The wood louse, or sow bug, is a small, oval-shaped, flat crustacean related to the crab and lobster. It belongs to the family Oniscidae. The wood louse has seven pairs of legs and lives in the bark of trees and old wood, or under stones. It can roll itself into a ball when threatened. It also does this sometimes during dry spells to preserve its water. The gribble is a similar crustacean that lives in the sea. It destroys piers and the timbers of ships. *See also* CRUSTACEAN.   W.R.P./C.S.H.

The woodpecker drills holes in trees to capture insects living inside the trees. Most woodpeckers nest in large holes which they dig in the branches or trunks of trees.

WOODPECKER (wȕd′ pek′ ər) A woodpecker is a bird that is a member of the family Picidae. It is called a woodpecker because it "pecks" into wood, looking for insects to eat. The bill of the bird is long and narrow. It has a chisellike tip to help drill holes into dead or unhealthy trees. The woodpecker then uses its long tongue to capture and eat the insects living inside these trees. Most woodpeckers nest in large holes that they dig in the branches or trunks of trees.

There are 24 species of woodpeckers found in North America. These include the flickers and sapsuckers. (*See* FLICKER; SAP-SUCKER.) There is much variation in size. The downy woodpecker, common through much of the continent, can grow to 14 cm [5.5 in] long. The pileated woodpecker, found in the eastern and northwestern United States and in parts of Canada, often reaches a length of 34 cm [13 in]. The pileated woodpecker chisels large, deep, oblong holes into the trunks of trees.   S.R.G./L.L.S.

WOOD'S METAL (wu̇dz′ met′ əl) Wood's metal is an alloy containing bismuth, lead, tin, and cadmium. (*See* ALLOY.) Wood's metal has the extremely low melting point of about 70°C [158°F], which is less than the boiling point of water.

Practical jokers make spoons of Wood's metal and give them to guests to stir hot drinks. The spoons soon melt. A serious use for Wood's metal is for the fusible plug in sprinkler fire-extinguishing systems. If a fire occurs, the plug melts and lets water run to a number of outlet nozzles.   J.J.A./A.D.

WOODY PLANT (wu̇d′ ē plant′) A woody plant is either a shrub or a tree. It has a hard, stiff stem that contains large amounts of woody xylem. (*See* STEM.) Its cell walls are thickened with cellulose and lignin, two substances that add great strength to the cells. There are also many woody fibers stretching throughout the plant. Most woody plants are perennial (grow for several years). *See also* HERBACEOUS PLANT; SHRUB; TREE; WOOD; XYLEM.   A.J.C./M.H.S.

WOOL (wu̇l′) Wool is a fiber that usually comes from the protective covering, or fleece, of sheep. Types of wool are determined by the sheep's fleece. The quality depends on the age and the physical condition of the animal and the climate in which it lives. The fleece of a healthy sheep is covered by yolk. Yolk is an oily substance consisting of wool grease and dried perspiration. Yolk protects the sheep from rain. It also keeps the fleece from becoming matted or tangled. Young sheep produce the best wool. Low-quality wool comes from dead or diseased sheep.

The processing of wool involves four main steps. The first is shearing. Most sheep shearers use power shears. Experts can clip 200 or more animals a day. The second step involves grading and sorting. Workers remove any stained or damaged wool from each fleece. They then sort the rest of the wool according to the quality of the fibers. Wool fibers are judged by their strength, fineness, length, waviness, and color. The third step is concerned with making yarn. After the wool is cleaned and dried, it is carded. Carding involves passing the wool through rollers that have thin wire teeth. The teeth untangle the fibers and arrange them into a flat sheet called a web. The web is formed into narrow ropes called slivers. The slivers are stretched into thinner strands called roving. Spinning machines twist the roving into yarn. Woolen yarn is bulky and fuzzy. Worsted yarn is smooth and highly twisted.

The fourth and final step involves making fabric. Wool manufactures knit or weave yarn into a variety of fabrics. Woolen yarns are used in making flannel, Shetland, and tweed fabrics. Worsted yarns are used for fabrics such as gabardine, sharkskin, and twill.

Wool may be dyed at various stages of the manufacturing process. All wool fabrics undergo finishing processes to give them a certain look and feel. *See also* SHEEP; TEXTILE.   J.J.A./M.H.S.

WORM (wərm′) Worm is the common name for a large and varied group of legless animals which have soft, slender bodies. These animals do not have backbones or notochords. (*See* NOTOCHORD.) Some worms, such as

earthworms, have hollow body spaces. The internal organs are contained in these spaces. Worms vary greatly in size. Some are less than 1mm [0.04 in] long. Giant earthworms are longer than 3 m [10 ft]. Some roundworms live in rotting animal and plant matter. Many worms live as parasites in human beings, animals, and plants. (*See* PARASITE.) Flukes, tapeworms, and pinworms are among the parasites of human beings.

The larvae of butterflies and other insects are often thought of as worms. But zoologists consider only certain adult animals as true worms. (A zoologist is a scientist who studies animal life.) Helminthology is the study of flatworms and roundworms.

Most true worms belong to four large groups. They are Platyhelminthes, Aschelminthes, Nemertinea, and Annelida. (*See* ANNELIDA; ASCHELMINTHES; NEMATODE; PLATYHELMINTHES.) *See also* EARTHWORM; LEECH; PROBOSCIS WORM; TAPEWORM.

J.J.A./C.S.H.

WREN (ren) A wren is a small bird that belongs to the family Troglodytidae. It is mostly brown with a long, thin bill. The wren often hops from branch to branch with its tail tilted upward.

A winter wren (below left) is about 10 cm [about 4 in] long. A house wren (below right) is about 12.5 cm [about 5 in] long. Wrens are perching birds. They are known for their loud songs.

There are nine species of wrens in North America. They are found in many types of habitats—forests, deserts, marshes, and meadows. Wrens eat insects and are known for their loud and pretty songs. Most wrens are between 7.5 and 11.7 cm [3 to 4.75 in] in length.

S.R.G./L.L.S.

WRIGHT BROTHERS Wilbur (1867–1912) and Orville (1871–1948) Wright—the Wright (rīt) Brothers—invented, built, and flew the first powered airplane. The world's first flight in a heavier-than-air, power-driven machine occurred on December 17, 1903, at Kitty Hawk, North Carolina. Orville won the toss of a coin and had the honor of piloting the airplane on its first flight. He flew 37 m [120 ft] and remained in the air for 12 seconds. Three more flights were made that day. The longest by Wilbur was 260 m [853 ft] in 59 seconds.

The flights were scarcely noticed by the world. Only three or four newspapers reported it the next day, and those reports were inaccurate. The Wright Brothers, themselves, did not foresee how the airplane would change civilization.

The brothers built that first plane for less than $1,000. Its two wings were 12 m [40.5 ft] long, and the craft weighed about 340 kg [750 lb] including the pilot. A small gasoline engine of their own design drove a two-bladed propeller.

The Wrights continued to experiment with airplanes after 1903. Wilbur went to France in 1908 and made flights to altitudes of

91 m [300 ft] and more. Orville made 57 complete circles at an altitude of 37 m [120 ft] above the drill field at Fort Myer, Virginia. In 1912, Wilbur died of typhoid fever, and Orville continued to work alone. He opened the Wright Aeronautical Laboratory in 1916 and was a pioneer in many developments in aviation. In 1929, he accepted the Daniel Guggenheim Medal for Wilbur's and his contributions to aviation. Orville died in 1948. Today, the original plane used at Kitty Hawk hangs in the National Air and Space Museum in Washington, D.C. *See also* AVIATION, HISTORY OF. W.R.P./D.G.F.

WROUGHT IRON (ròt īrn) Wrought iron is a very pure form of iron. (*See* IRON.) It is made by purifying molten pig iron in a special furnace called a puddling furnace. The furnace is made so that heat is reflected down on to the iron from its low roof. The high temperature removes impurities such as carbon, sulfur, phosphorus, and silicon. The wrought iron that is made contains less than 0.3 percent carbon. The metal is malleable (readily hammered into shape) and ductile (easily pulled out into rods or wires). The wrought iron contains a small proportion of the impurities called slag. The slag content makes the iron more resistant to corrosion than ordinary iron. Wrought iron was once widely used. However, it has now been replaced by steel for many purposes. D.M.H.W./A.I.

XANTHOPHYLL (zan′ thə fil′) Xanthophyll, or lutein, is a yellowish orange pigment found in plants and egg yolks. It is an organic compound with the chemical formula $C_{40}H_{56}O_2$. Xanthophylls exist in large numbers in many leaves where, with the green pigment chlorophyll, they have a role in photosynthesis. (*See* CHLOROPHYLL.) Leaves are usually green because the chlorophyll masks the xanthophyll. In the fall, however, the chlorophyll begins to decrease and the xanthophyll shows through. This gives the leaves a yellow or orange color. Xanthophyll also gives color to some algae and to the yellow petals of many flowers. *See also* CAROTENE; PIGMENT. A.J.C./M.H.S.

XENON (zē′ nän′) Xenon is an element belonging to the noble gas group of elements. The gas has the atomic weight 131.30, and its atomic number is 54. It has a melting point of −111.9°C [−169.4°F] and a boiling point of −108.1°C [−162.5°F]. Its symbol is Xe.

Xenon is a very rare gas. It makes up only about one part in twelve million of the atmosphere. It is odorless and colorless and almost completely unreactive. It does form a few compounds, including fluorides. It is used to fill flash lamps and electron tubes. The element is obtained by fractional distillation from liquid air. (*See* DISTILLATION.) The gas was discovered by the British chemists Sir William Ramsay and Morris Travers in 1898. It was named for the Greek word *xenos*, meaning stranger. D.M.H.W./J.D.

XEROGRAPHY (zə räg′ rə fē) Xerography is a means of copying documents without the use of liquids. Its name means ''dry writing.'' Xerography uses static electricity. It also relies upon the properties of the element selenium. (*See* SELENIUM.) When light shines on a surface of selenium, its resistance to the passage of an electric current drops sharply.

To copy a document or the page of a book, the operator places it, face down, upon a horizontal glass window. The machine is started by pressing a button. A bright light shines on the document, and an image of it is projected by means of a lens onto a highly polished cylindrical drum. The drum is coated with a layer of the metal selenium. The drum is charged with static electricity.

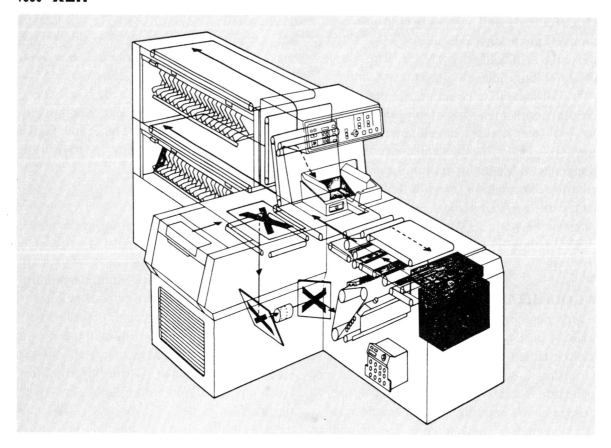

A cutaway view of a xerographic copying machine is shown above. Xerography is a means of copying documents with the use of liquids. Xerography uses static electricity.

Where light is reflected from the white parts of the document on the drum, the electrical resistance of the drum drops. The electrostatic charge on the selenium is leaked away to the ground. Where light does not reach the drum, because the writing or dark areas of the document have absorbed it, then the static charge on the drum remains. The cylinder is then covered with special powdered black ink. The ink adheres to the drum where there is still an electrostatic charge. In this way an image of the document is formed in powdered ink on the drum.

Next, a sheet of plain white paper is passed close to the drum. An electrostatic charge opposite to that on the drum is produced under the paper. This attracts the ink powder from the drum. It jumps from the drum so that the image is transferred to the paper. The paper is heated before it leaves the machine. This makes the ink melt and stick permanently to the paper, giving a reproduction of the original document.

D.M.H.W./J.D.

XEROPHYTE (zir′ ə fīt′) Xerophytes are plants that are specially adapted so that they can live in hot, dry places such as deserts. (*See* ADAPTATION.) Deserts cover about 20 percent of the land on earth. Some deserts, such as parts of the Sahara Desert in Africa, have hardly any plant life. In most deserts, though, there is a variety of small, widely separated plants.

Most xerophytes have extensive, spreading roots near the surface so they can absorb as much water as possible after even a light rainfall. Xerophytes usually have thick, protective cuticles and small, often highly modified, leaves. (*See* LEAF.) The stomata are usually few in number and are somehow shielded or protected from the sun and wind. Many have thick stems or other modified structures for storing water. Members of the cactus family are good examples of xerophytes.

Some plants that grow in hot, dry places are not true xerophytes. Some desert plants grow quickly after a heavy rain. They scatter seeds before the sand dries and they die. Some desert shrubs have long roots which reach down to underground water supplies. *See also* CACTUS FAMILY; PLANT KINGDOM.

A.J.C./M.H.S.

X RAYS (eks′ rāz′) X rays are very energetic waves of electromagnetic energy. (*See* ELECTROMAGNETIC RADIATION.) They are members of the same family as light waves, gamma rays, and radio waves. The waves have a much greater frequency than light waves and are invisible. Their frequency is less than that of gamma rays, which are also invisible.

X rays were discovered by Professor Wilhelm Konrad Roentgen (also written Röntgen) in 1895. He did not know what they were, and so he called them X rays, because x stands for an unknown quantity.

X rays are produced when electrons traveling at high speed hit the surface of something composed of heavy atoms. The fast

This clear radiogram of a flatfish (below) was produced with a modern X-ray machine.

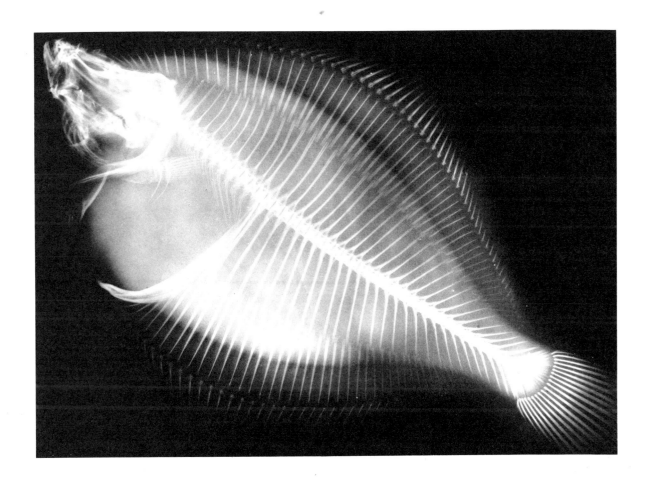

electrons lose energy and give out X rays. They also change the energy of the electrons already in the atoms. This causes the release of energy in the form of X rays of different frequencies. An X-ray tube is a vacuum tube in which a heated cathode is used to produce electrons. The electrons are then speeded up by means of a high voltage until they strike the anode, which is known as the "target." From the anode, X rays are produced and can be directed in any direction that is wanted.

Different ranges of X rays of various frequencies can be produced by changing the voltage that speeds the electrons or the substance of which the target anode is made. When there is a mixture of different X-ray frequencies, the X rays are said to be "white" radiation. X rays that have very high frequencies are called "hard" radiation, and X rays with lower frequencies are called "soft" radiation.

The best-known property of X rays is their ability to pass through many forms of matter. Other properties include the way in which they ionize gases when they pass through them, and the way in which they cause fluorescent materials to glow. (*See* IONS AND IONIZATION; FLUORESCENCE.) X rays also affect photographic film.

X rays passing into dense materials are absorbed more readily than X rays passing into lighter materials. For this reason, X rays have been used in medicine almost since the time of their discovery. They can be used to show up different internal structures and reveal broken bones or foreign objects in the tissues. (*See* RADIOGRAPHY.)

X rays have a damaging effect on the body's cells. They can be used to destroy unwanted cells in the body and are therefore useful for the treatment of cancer. However, they must be used under carefully controlled conditions. (*See* RADIOTHERAPY.)

In physics, the use of X rays helps to reveal the structure of atoms, molecules, and crystals. (*See* X-RAY DIFFRACTION.)

D.M.H.W./J.D.

Early X-ray machines, such as the one pictured above, produced crude radiograms. For almost 100 years, X-ray machines have been used to reveal bone fractures and diseased tissues. X-rays were discovered by Professor Wilhelm Konrad Roentgen in 1895. He did not know what they were and called them X rays—x stands for unknown quantity.

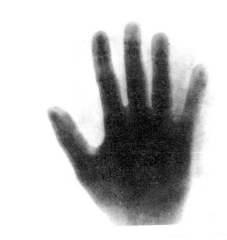

This radiogram of a hand (above) was produced with an early X-ray machine.

X-RAY DIFFRACTION (eks′ rā′ dif rak′ shən) X-ray diffraction is the scattering of radiation that occurs when a beam of X rays is directed at an object. The atoms and molecules in a crystal have a regular pattern. X rays have a much shorter wavelength than visible light and are affected by the crystal in much the same way that light can be diffracted by a diffraction grating. (*See* DIFFRACTION). As X rays pass through a crystal, the pattern or lattice of the crystal changes the beam of X rays, breaking it up into a regular pattern. If a photographic plate is put on the other side of the crystal, the pattern shows up as regularly spaced dots. From this pattern, it is possible to find out a great deal about the structure of the crystal. This technique is called X-ray crystallography. (*See* CRYSTAL.)

The pattern produced by a particular substance is characteristic of that substance. X-ray diffraction can therefore be used to analyze substances to see what they contain. The method can also be used to try to determine why certain substances have certain properties, such as elasticity, or viscosity, or hardness.

The use of X rays to study crystals was first suggested by the German physicist Max von Laue in 1912. *See also* X RAY.

D.M.H.W./J.D.

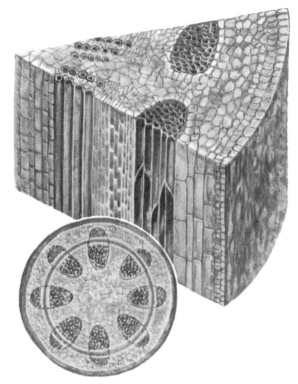

A segment of a small tree branch (top) shows the tubes of xylem which conduct water through the plant. The smaller cross section (bottom) of a one-year-old twig shows how xylem develops inward from the cambium (inner ring), which is the main living tissue of the tree trunk and branches. Xylem is a system of tubes made up of dead cells with thick, wood walls, which contain large amounts of cellulose and lignin. Xylem is surrounded by many fibers that give support to the plant.

XYLEM (zī′ ləm) Xylem is the vascular tissue that carries water and dissolved minerals from the roots to the leaves. It is a system of tubes made up of dead cells with thick, woody walls. These walls contain large amounts of cellulose and lignin. Xylem is surrounded by many fibers that extend along its length. This structure gives a great deal of support to the plant.

In ferns and gymnosperms, xylem is made of tapering, tube-shaped cells called tracheids. The walls of the tracheids have many tiny pits, or holes, to allow water and dissolved minerals to pass from one cell to the next. In angiosperms, however, xylem is made of long, tubular vessels. These vessels are made of cells whose ends have disintegrated, leaving a continuous tube. *See also* VASCULAR PLANT; WOOD.

A.J.C./M.H.S.

YAK (yak) The yak (*Bos grunniens*) is a shaggy wild ox found in Asia, especially in the mountains of Tibet. The yak stands about 1.8 m [6 ft] at the shoulder. The animal weighs from 499 to 544 kg [1,100 to 1,200

lb]. Yaks are covered with black or brownish hair. The hair is very long and silky. (*See* HAIR.)

Though the yak is heavily built, it is quite agile. It can slide down icy slopes, swim rivers, and cross steep rock slides. If forced to defend itself, a yak can gather up a tremendous charge. Hunting has caused the killing of many wild yaks. The animal is now in danger of extinction.

The yak has been domesticated. The domesticated yak is often called the grunting ox. It is the result of many generations of careful breeding. It is usually white or piebald. Domesticated yaks are smaller than the wild ones. The domesticated ones are often used as pack animals. Also, their soft hair is used to make cloth. The coarse hair is used to make mats and tent coverings. Saddles, boots, and other articles are made from the hides.
J.J.A./J.J.M.

YAM (yam) The yam is a vegetable plant that has thick roots similar to those of the sweet potato. It belongs to the yam family Dioscoreaceae. These thick roots or tubers are a major food source in many tropical areas. The tubers, which are shaped like large pears, contain water, sugar, and starch and taste very much like a sweet potato. The plant grows climbing vines that bear small, green flower clusters.

Most of the world's yam crop is grown in western Africa. India, Southeast Asia, and the Caribbean Islands are other areas where yams are important crops. A few yams are grown in the southern part of the United States.
W.R.P./F.W.S.

YEAST (yēst) Yeast is the common name for about 160 types of one-celled fungi. Yeasts reproduce quickly both asexually by budding or fission and sexually by producing gametes which join to form a zygote. Yeasts feed on sugar and, in the absence of air, convert it into carbon dioxide (a gas) and alcohol. For this reason, yeasts are used in many types of breads, beers, and wines.

In baking, yeasts are used to make the dough rise. Some of the enzymes produced by yeast convert starch in the flour into sugar. (*See* ENZYME.) Other enzymes from the yeasts change this sugar into carbon dioxide and alcohol. (*See* FERMENTATION.) The carbon dioxide forms bubbles which cause the dough to increase in size, or rise. Since these enzymes work only within a limited temperature range—about 27° to 29°C [80° to 85°F]—the dough must be kept warm in order to rise. When the dough is baked, the alcohol evaporates and the yeasts are killed. As a result, baked bread should not have any yeast or alcohol taste.

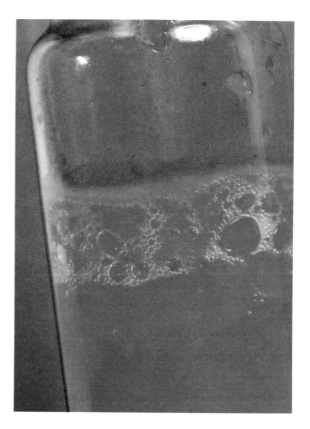

Yeasts feed on sugar and, in the absence of air, convert it into carbon dioxide and alcohol. Frothing (above), caused by carbon dioxide, is shown in the fermentation of a fruit pulp. When yeast ferments sugars, turning them into alcohol, it releases carbon dioxide gas which causes the liquid to froth.

Yeasts are present in the air almost everywhere. In the past, bakers collected yeasts by leaving a mixture of flour, sugar, and water uncovered for a few hours. Although some people still use this method, most prefer to buy commercially prepared yeasts. Yeasts are sold in grocery stores in two forms: dry and compressed. Dry yeast is inactive yeast cells. It can be stored indefinitely and is activated by adding warm water and sugar (or starch). Compressed yeast, however, contains active yeast cells, moisture, and starch. Compressed yeast lasts for a relatively short time and must be kept refrigerated until used. *See also* FUNGUS.

A.J.C./E.R.L.

YELLOW FEVER (yel′ ō fēv′ ər) Yellow fever is a virus disease. (*See* VIRUS.) It damages many tissues in the human body, especially the liver. Such damage makes the liver unable to work properly. Yellow pigments appear in the skin. This is how yellow fever gets its name. Walter Reed, a United States Army doctor, proved that yellow fever was carried by a mosquito. Reed suggested that the cause was a microorganism. Three research physicians later proved that the microorganism was a virus.

In most cases, a type of mosquito (*Aëdes aegypti*) carries the yellow fever virus from one person to another. A mosquito infected with the virus can transmit the disease for the rest of its life.

Symptoms of yellow fever include fever, headache, dizziness, and muscle pain. If the disease progresses beyond this stage, the skin turns yellow. The victim bleeds from the gums and stomach lining. Some patients go into a coma. Death often follows the coma. About 3 percent of all cases of yellow fever result in death.

Yellow fever can be prevented with a vaccine developed in 1937 by Max Theiler, a South African research physician.

J.J.A./J.J.F.

YEW (yü) Yew are eight species of evergreen trees and shrubs that belong to genus *Taxus* of the yew family. They have dark green, needlelike leaves arranged in spirals on the spreading branches. The reproductive structures are conelike on the male plants and very small and green on the female plants. (*See* DIOECIOUS.) They are not true cones, however. Single seeds are enclosed in a fleshy red aril. The bark, leaves, and seeds, but not the arils, are poisonous.

Most yews grow in temperate areas of the Northern Hemisphere. The trees often grow to a height of 25 m [80 ft]. They grow slowly and may live for hundreds of years. Yew wood is hard and beautifully grained. It is used in making fine furniture, archery bows, and small carved objects. A.J.C./M.H.S.

YTTERBIUM (i tər′ bē əm) Ytterbium is a metallic element. It belongs to a group known as the rare earth elements. The metal has the atomic number 70, and its atomic weight is 173.04. Its chemical symbol is Yb. Ytterbium melts at 824°C [1,515°F] and boils at 1,193°C [2,179°F]. It has a valence of two or three in its compounds.

The element is found in the mineral gadolinite. It was discovered by the Swiss chemist Jean de Marignac in 1878. It was named for the Swedish village of Ytterby.

D.M.H.W./J.D.

YTTRIUM (i′ trē əm) Yttrium is a metallic element similar to the rare earth elements. It has the atomic number 39, and its atomic weight is 88.905. Its chemical symbol is Y. Yttrium melts at 1,523°C [2,773°F] and boils at 3,337°C [6,039°F]. It has a valence of three in its compounds. In appearance it resembles iron.

Yttrium occurs in the minerals gadolinite, xenotime, fergusonite, and euxenite. It was discovered by the Finnish chemist Johann Gadolin in 1794. It is named after the village of Ytterby in Sweden. *See also* RARE EARTH ELEMENT. D.M.H.W./J.D.

YUCCA (yək′ ə) Yucca is a group of plants native to southwestern United States and Mexico. The 40 species of yucca belong to the lily family.

The yucca plant (above) has fragrant flowers which open up at night. Yucca plants are native to southwestern United States and Mexico. This plant was used by the American Indians for food and clothing.

Although many yucca plants are stemless, some have stems 10 m [33 ft] high. The sword-shaped leaves grow in clusters along or at the tip of the stem. The bell-shaped flowers range in color from whitish green to white to cream colored. The flowers grow in the center of a leaf cluster. The flowers emit a strong odor when they open at night. The yucca fruit contains many black seeds.

Yuccas can only be pollinated by a certain group of moths. Each species of yucca moths can only pollinate a certain species of yucca. (*See* POLLINATION.)

The yucca plant was used by the American Indians for food and clothing. The yucca is the state flower of New Mexico. *See also* LILY FAMILY. J.M.C./M.H.S.

Z

ZEBRA (zēb′ rə) The zebra is an African member of the horse family. It is easily recognized by its striped coat. This color pattern makes the zebra different from all other members of the horse family. The parallel black or dark brown stripes on white are arranged in exact designs. The stripes run all over the body, meeting in a diagonal pattern at the head. The stripes help to hide the zebra from its enemies by blending into the patterns of shadow and sunlight where it lives. (*See* CAMOUFLAGE; PROTECTIVE COLORATION.) The lion is the zebra's main enemy.

Zebras are grazing animals. Some kinds of zebras roam open grassy plains. Others live in rough mountains. Zebras live in small bands. Each group is led by a stallion. Zebras are noted fighters. They are difficult to tame and train. Great numbers of zebras have been killed for their meat and hides. Some kinds of zebras are nearly extinct, and others are numerous. Although there is some confusion about the number of species of zebras, it is generally considered that there are three: the mountain zebra (*Equus zebra*), Burchell's zebra (*Equus burchelli*), and Grevy's zebra

A group of Burchell's zebras (*Equus burchelli*) are shown above.

(*Equus grevyi*). Burchell's zebras are the most common.   J.J.A./J.J.M.

ZENITH (zē′ nəth) A zenith is the point on the celestial sphere directly over an observer. The geographical zenith is the point where a line, passing through the center of the earth and the observer, crosses the celestial sphere. *See also* CELESTIAL SPHERE.   J.M.C./C.R.

ZEOLITE (zē′ ə līt) Zeolites are a group of minerals. They are silicates of aluminum and sodium or calcium. They contain between 10 and 20 percent water, which is readily given up when the minerals are heated. This leaves ''holes'' in the crystal structure of the zeolite. Other molecules or ions can be absorbed by the zeolite and trapped in these holes. For this reason zeolites are sometimes called ''molecular sieves.'' Zeolites are often used for softening water. (*See* WATER SOFTENING.) Zeolites can be made artificially by heating clay, sand, and sodium carbonate.

D.M.H.W./J.D.

ZERO GRAVITY *See* WEIGHTLESSNESS.

ZINC (zingk) Zinc (Zn) is a chemical element with an atomic number of 30. Its atomic weight is 65.37. Zinc has a melting point of 419.58°C [787.24°F]. The element boils at 907°C [1,664.6°F].

Zinc is a bluish white metal. Zinc metal is never found pure in nature. It often occurs combined with sulfur in a mineral called zinc blende or sphalerite. This ore is found in Britain, Australia, Africa, and the United States.

A coating of zinc is often applied to metals, such as iron or steel, to prevent rusting. The coated metal is called ''galvanized'' iron or steel. The galvanized metal is used for products such as roof gutters.

Zinc is often combined with other metals to form alloys. Brass is an alloy of copper and zinc. Bronze is copper, tin, and zinc. Nickel silver is copper, nickel, and zinc. (*See* BRASS; BRONZE; NICKEL.) The alloy Prestal, made of zinc and aluminum, has the strength of steel, but can be molded like plastic.

Moist air discolors zinc with a coating of zinc oxide (ZnO). After a thin layer of this coating forms, the air cannot tarnish the zinc below it. White powdery zinc oxide is a very useful chemical in industry. It is used in the manufacture of cosmetics, plastics, rubber, and soaps. The chemical is also used as a pigment in paints and inks.

Zinc sulfide (ZnS) is luminescent and is used on luminous dials for clocks and to make luminous paints. (*See* LUMINESCENCE.) It is also used to coat the inside of the television screens. Zinc chloride ($ZnCl_2$) in a water solution preserves wood from decay and protects it from insects.

Zinc is used in electric batteries. It is also used in solders. Zinc and its alloys are used in die casting, electroplating, and powder metallurgy. (*See* DIE; ELECTROPLATING; METAL AND METALLURGY.) J.J.A./J.R.W.

ZIRCONIUM (zǝr' kō' nē ǝm) Zirconium is a metallic element. It has the atomic number 40, and its atomic weight is 91.22. Zirconium melts at 1,850°C [3,362°F] and boils at 3,578°C [6,472°F]. The chemical symbol for zirconium is Zr. It has a valence of two, three, and four in its compounds.

Zirconium is a soft white metal. It can be used to make fuel containers for nuclear reactors. Zirconia or zirconium oxide (ZrO_2) withstands very high temperatures. It is used to make furnace linings and crucibles. Zirconium is found in the mineral zircon, which contains zirconium silicate. It was discovered by the German chemist Marti Klaproth in 1789. It is named for the gemstone zircon in which it occurs. D.M.H.W./J.D.

ZODIAC (zōd' ē ak') The zodiac is a band of twelve constellations that lie on either side of the ecliptic. The ecliptic is the sun's apparent path through the heavens. The constellations of the zodiac are: Aquarius, Pisces, Aries, Taurus, Gemini, Cancer, Leo, Virgo, Libra, Scorpio, Sagittarius, and Capricorn.

Each constellation of the zodiac was given a certain time period by ancient astronomers. These periods corresponded to the times when the sun was in a particular zodiac constella-

A specimen of zinc ore (left) is shown. Zinc is used as a protective coating for iron and steel objects. It is often combined with other metals to form alloys.

tion. However, they are no longer accurate because of slight changes of the earth's axis. (*See* PRECESSION.)

Many people think that the zodiac constellations have an influence on their lives. Such people follow the beliefs of astrology. *See also* ASTROLOGY, CONSTELLATION.

J.M.C./C.R.

ZOO

A zoo (zü), or zoological garden, is a parklike place where living animals are kept and displayed. In zoos, people can see and learn about wild animals from throughout the world. Many zoos sponsor special tours, educational activities, and magazines or newsletters. Zoos serve as "living laboratories" where scientists can study the anatomy, physiology, and behavior of animals. In recent years, zoos have played an important role in wildlife conservation, particularly for rare or endangered species.

Types of zoos There are more than 600 zoos throughout the world. Most are located in or near large cities. Some large zoos have thousands of wild animals—mammals, birds, reptiles, amphibians, fish, and insects—from throughout the world. The world's largest zoo, the San Diego Zoo in California, has more than 5,000 animals representing about 1,600 species and subspecies. Most zoos have a more limited, though worldwide, collection. Some zoos specialize in one group of animals. The Arizona-Sonora Desert Museum in Tucson, Arizona, for example, exhibits only animals that live in the Sonora Desert. The New England Aquarium in Boston, Massachusetts, has more than 450 species of fish on display.

Children's zoos throughout the country allow children (and adults) to see and actually touch tame animals. Though most of these animals are domestic animals such as goats, some children's zoos also have baby wild animals such as elephants and monkeys.

Since the 1960s, drive-through, or safari, zoos have become popular. In these zoos, animals wander freely through large, open areas. People can drive through these areas in their cars or, in many cases, in buses or monorails operated by the zoos. The largest of these zoos is the San Diego Wild Animal Park which covers 728 hectares [1,800 acres] in southern California.

Display and care of animals In the past, zoos crowded animals into small, dark, dirty cages. Shock, disease, and poor treatment killed many of the animals within a few months after their arrival at a zoo. Modern zoos, however, are different. Animals are displayed in settings that often are quite similar to their homes in the wild. Many animals are no longer kept in cages. They live in large areas with trees, plants, pools of water, and, in some cases, waterfalls. These areas are usually surrounded by deep ditches, or moats, which keep the animals from leaving their "island." The Bronx Zoo in New York City was the first to enclose many different animals in one area. In its *African Plains* section, the zoo has birds, reptiles, and mammals that normally live together in Africa. Many other zoos now use this same concept.

Birds are usually displayed in large, enclosed areas called aviaries. Some of these aviaries are enclosed by vertical strands of thin wire which, at a distance, cannot be seen. It was recently discovered that if a large area had many trees and plants, and plenty of sunlight, the birds nested and tended not to leave these "natural" aviaries.

Animals that would not normally survive the weather and temperature of the zoo are kept in special, climate-controlled buildings that imitate conditions in the wild. Many animals are active at night and sleep during the day. (*See* NOCTURNAL HABIT.) Some zoos have solved this problem by keeping these animals in bright, white light at night and in red light during the day. This makes the animals switch their cycles so that they are active during the day when the zoo has most of its visitors. (*See* BIOLOGICAL RHYTHM.) Most larger zoos have a full time medical staff that examines and treats the animals. (*See* VETERINARY MEDICINE.) Some zoos even have a hospital for sick animals and a nursery for baby animals. All the animals are fed specially designed diets to meet their nutritional needs. Some animals, such as birds, are fed several times a day while others, such as some reptiles, may be fed only once or twice a week. All zoos have a trained, professional staff that watches over the animals and ensures their safety. Most zoos also have trained guides to lead tours or provide information about the animals.

History of zoos Since prehistoric times, people have kept animals for display. The earliest zoo was established in Egypt in about 1500 B.C. Several hundred years later, the Greeks used zoos as places where students could learn about animals and plants. During the times of religious persecution, the Romans kept wild animals for use in the fights in the Colosseum. Many wealthy Romans even established their own personal zoos. During the Middle Ages, zoos, like all types of science, were generally ignored. As a result, there were very few collections of living wild animals at that time. In 1519, the Spaniards found a large zoo that had been established by the Aztec Indians in Mexico. Although small zoos were started throughout Europe during the next 200 years, most were unpopular because the animals were treated so badly.

The oldest zoo still in existence is the Schönbrunn Zoo, established in Austria in 1752. The Madrid (Spain) Zoo opened in 1775. The Paris (France) Zoo was established in 1793. The first true zoo, however, was started in 1829 by the Zoological Society of London. This zoo was the first to have animals from all parts of the world.

The first zoo in the United States was the Central Park Zoo in New York City. It opened in 1854 and is still in operation. The Philadelphia Zoo opened in 1874. It started the world's first children's zoo in 1938. The only federally funded zoo in the United States was established by Congress in 1889. It is the National Zoological Park in Washington, D.C. The first Canadian zoo opened in Toronto in 1887. By 1900, there were zoos in several major North American cities. There are more than 150 zoos throughout the United States and Canada. There are at least 400 zoos in other countries of the world. *See also* ZOOLOGY. A.J.C./R.J.B.

ZOOLOGY (zō äl′ ə jē) Zoology is the branch of biology that deals with the study of animals. There are at least 14 well-known areas of specialization within zoology. These include entomology (the study of insects), ornithology (the study of birds), taxonomy (the naming and classifying of animals), morphology (examining the form and structure of animals), pathology (the study of animal diseases), cytology (the study of body cells), histology (the study of body tissue structures), embryology (the study of the development of an animal from an egg), and comparative anatomy (the comparison of body structures of different animals). Genetics, physiology, ecology, psychology, and paleontology are other divisions. W.R.P./R.J.B.

ZYGOTE (zī′ gōt′) A zygote is a cell produced by the union of two gametes, or sex cells. (*See* GAMETE.) It is formed during sexual reproduction and is sometimes thought of as a fertilized egg. A zygote has the full (diploid) number of chromosomes—half from each gamete. A zygote can develop into an embryo which, in turn, develops into an adult organism. *See also* FERTILIZATION; REPRODUCTION. A.J.C./E.R.L.